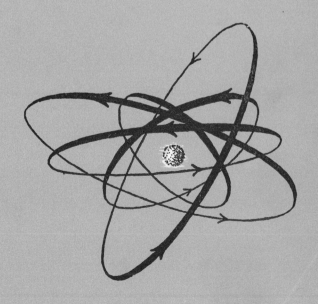

All About the ATOM

by IRA M. FREEMAN

If you could magnify a single grain of table salt until it became as big as the Empire State Building, each atom in it would look only as big as the grain you started with! And if you could place eighty million molecules in a row like marbles, they would stretch only the distance of an inch.

Yet unbelievably small as they are, both atoms and molecules arrange themselves in distinctive patterns in different kinds of material. All the while, they are constantly moving in a wild zigzag that is measured in billions of bumps a second.

In fact, the things that happen in the fantastic world of the atom sometimes sound like the wildest science fiction. But they have been tested and are true beyond a doubt. For scientists have learned to weigh and split the atom. They have traced the dizzy course of the molecule. And they have used this information in developing the greatest source of power the world has ever known. Yet for most people the atom is a great mystery.

For them, Dr. Ira M. Freeman has written *All About the Atom,* a simple and dramatic explanation of the atom and how it works. With vivid examples, this distinguished physicist explains what things are made of, how energy makes things go and how the atom idea was developed.

Readers of all ages will be thrilled by this fascinating explanation of the wonders of the atom.

Illustrated by GEORGE A. WILDE

An Allabout Book

RANDOM HOUSE • NEW YORK

All About
the Atom

By Ira M. Freeman

Illustrated by George Wilde

RANDOM HOUSE

NEW YORK

EIGHTH PRINTING

© COPYRIGHT 1955 BY IRA M. FREEMAN

MANUFACTURED IN THE UNITED STATES OF AMERICA

LIBRARY OF CONGRESS CATALOG CARD NUMBER: 55-6060

DEWEY DECIMAL CLASSIFICATION: 539

Contents

CHAPTER 1

What Are Things Made of?

If Abraham Lincoln could listen in on our conversations today, he would hear much that would puzzle him. Things have changed greatly in a hundred years' time. Now our famous visitor from the past would have difficulty understanding many of the things we take for granted. Words we use all the time would be entirely strange to him, yet such expressions as "sound barrier," "atomic energy," "streptomycin," and "radar" are in our newspapers every day. He might recognize from their sound that they were scientific terms, but that would be about all.

Today we know how much science affects our way of living. Out of much patient work have come better houses and clothing, marvelous drugs to fight disease, more nourishing and wholesome food, new kinds of entertainment and speedy forms of transportation.

This spread of science is really something quite new. Probably there always were a few thinkers who were interested in studying the world around them, but hardly anyone else ever learned about their ideas and activities. Still, from earliest times, people were curious about the things found in their surroundings. They wondered about the rocks under foot, the wood of the forest trees, the waters of the sea and the clouds floating in the air.

Later, as many more materials were found and became familiar, they were put into groups. Some, such as stone and iron, are called *solids*. Others are known as *liquids*, such as oil or water. Still others are called *gases* —for example, air or steam.

Think of a solid object as one that tries hard to keep a definite size and shape, like a brick or half dollar. A liquid, too, has definite size—it is almost impossible to squeeze it into any smaller space. But, unlike a solid, a liquid flows and takes on the shape of any container into which you pour it.

A gas, however, has neither size nor fixed shape. If some air, or other gas, is let into a bottle, it will evenly fill out the whole space inside the bottle no matter how much or how little gas is used. It moves right out to the

Solid   Liquid   Gas

All things can be put into three groups: solid, liquid or gas.

glass in all directions. Unlike water in a jar, a gas has no distinct surface of its own.

Many things are familiar to you in more than one of these forms. Water is probably the most common example. The water you drink is in its familiar liquid form. The ice cubes floating in it are water in its solid form. Escaping from the liquid all the time is water vapor, which is water in the form of a gas. The tiny drops of mist on the outside of the glass come from water vapor. It was in the air to begin with, but *condensed* into liquid water when it touched the cold glass. The steam from boiling water is also water vapor. It is just as invisible as air until it begins to cool and condense into a misty cloud you can see. At this point it should no longer be called steam, but fog or mist.

Other materials, too, can take all three forms. Heating

Smoke

Foam

Mud

These materials are mixtures of solid, liquid and gas.

or cooling often brings about the changes. At ordinary temperatures iron is solid. In a steel mill, when iron is heated to about 2,700 degrees, it becomes a liquid. Then it can be cast into any desired shape. On cooling it becomes solid again and keeps this shape. In the sun, where the temperature is over 10,000 degrees, iron is a gas. A chemist usually pays little attention to these changes in form. To him, iron is iron and water is water, whether it happens to be gas, liquid or solid.

Look at the things in your surroundings and try to decide which form each one has. Some materials turn out to be doubtful. For instance, a piece of pitch or sealing wax seems hard and brittle like any solid material. If it is hammered or dropped, it shatters like glass. But if you put

Foam

Smoke

Mud

These materials are mixtures of solid, liquid and gas.

or cooling often brings about the changes. At ordinary temperatures iron is solid. In a steel mill, when iron is heated to about 2,700 degrees, it becomes a liquid. Then it can be cast into any desired shape. On cooling it becomes solid again and keeps this shape. In the sun, where the temperature is over 10,000 degrees, iron is a gas. A chemist usually pays little attention to these changes in form. To him, iron is iron and water is water, whether it happens to be gas, liquid or solid.

Look at the things in your surroundings and try to decide which form each one has. Some materials turn out to be doubtful. For instance, a piece of pitch or sealing wax seems hard and brittle like any solid material. If it is hammered or dropped, it shatters like glass. But if you put

Solid Liquid Gas

All things can be put into three groups: solid, liquid or gas.

glass in all directions. Unlike water in a jar, a gas has no distinct surface of its own.

Many things are familiar to you in more than one of these forms. Water is probably the most common example. The water you drink is in its familiar liquid form. The ice cubes floating in it are water in its solid form. Escaping from the liquid all the time is water vapor, which is water in the form of a gas. The tiny drops of mist on the outside of the glass come from water vapor. It was in the air to begin with, but *condensed* into liquid water when it touched the cold glass. The steam from boiling water is also water vapor. It is just as invisible as air until it begins to cool and condense into a misty cloud you can see. At this point it should no longer be called steam, but fog or mist.

Other materials, too, can take all three forms. Heating

All about
THE ATOM

allabout books 10

By IRA M. FREEMAN

A fascinating explanation of
the atom and how it works...
told in simple language and
with vivid illustrations

Illustrated by GEORGE WILDE

one of the pieces in a tin can and leave it for a few months, you find it has flowed and spread over the bottom. This time, it acts just like a liquid! Over a long time, even glass and some other solid-appearing substances will flow.

And what about foam and smoke and mud and fog? These are all mixtures. Smoke is made up of tiny solid particles floating in air, and mud consists of little solid bits floating in water. Later on in this book you will see how science has been able to clear up some of these questions by finding out more definitely what materials are made of. Scientists use the word *matter* when they speak of substances in general.

CHAPTER 2

Energy Makes Things Go

You soon realize that there are other things in our surroundings besides matter in its different forms. The pot warming on the range is different from the same pot when cold. Scientists say it contains heat. A fluorescent lamp is made of solid metal wires and of glass (really a liquid, remember). It is filled with a mixture of gases. Besides all this, electricity somehow plays a part. And, of course, the lamp gives off something that is called light. Things like heat, electricity or light are not matter because they do not exist in different forms and do not take up space. They cannot be weighed out or put up in packages like sugar or milk. They are different kinds of something that is called *energy*.

Energy is what makes matter *change*. Heat energy can change water from a solid to a liquid to a gas, as you already know. Light energy can fade the dye in your jacket or form an image on the film in your camera. Electrical energy can turn the motor of a vacuum cleaner, send your voice over a wire or bring you pictures of what is happening thousands of miles away.

There are other kinds of energy, too. The chemical energy in coal or oil heats houses and runs trains. The chemical energy of food runs your body, which is a sort

There are many kinds of energy in different forms.

of engine. The action of *atomic energy* is known, in a general way, to all of us.

Probably the most familiar kind of energy is the one that can make things move, or change their motion. This is called *mechanical energy*. A machine of any kind puts mechanical energy to work for some useful purpose. The machine may be a simple hand tool such as a hammer, or it may be as complicated as a printing press or locomotive.

If you place your hand on the table and carefully rest the head of a hammer on your thumb, nothing unusual happens. But if you accidentally hit your thumb with the same hammer while trying to drive a nail, a painful bruise results. The moving hammer-head is not at all the same thing as the hammer-head at rest. What makes it different is energy. The mechanical energy belonging to any moving object is called *kinetic energy*. A landslide, the flood waters of a river or the air in a hurricane are destructive because they have large amounts of kinetic energy.

Scientists know how to measure kinetic energy. You might expect that an automobile going 40 miles an hour would have just twice as much kinetic energy as one moving only 20 miles an hour. Actually, at 40 miles an

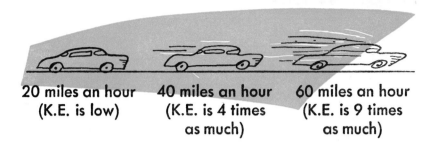

20 miles an hour
(K.E. is low)

40 miles an hour
(K.E. is 4 times
as much)

60 miles an hour
(K.E. is 9 times
as much)

The faster a car goes the greater the kinetic energy.

hour the car has 2 x 2 or *four* times as much energy as at the lower speed. At 60 miles per hour it would have 3 x 3 or *nine* times as much, and so on. Energy goes up very fast as the speed increases. You can see, then, why a collision at high speed is so destructive.

In order to set things going—to give them kinetic energy—you have to do some work on them. Often this work is done by your own muscles. A coaster wagon must be shoved, a stone thrown, a football kicked. This is the price you pay for getting anything going. But once the work has been done, it is stored in the moving object in the form of kinetic energy, propelling the wagon along the road and speeding the stone or football through the air.

Instead of giving the wagon a strong shove at the start, you could make it move across your back yard by pushing it slowly the whole way. This time there would be no kinetic energy stored up in the wagon at the beginning. In place of this, you would do work on it all along the way, supplying the energy just as it is needed to keep the wagon going.

There is still another way to move the wagon across the yard. Suppose there is a little hill at one end. You could push the wagon to the top of the hill, then let it roll down to the desired place. Notice that here again you have to do work in pushing the wagon up the hill. Energy always must be paid for—Nature sees to that.

Suppose you do not let the wagon coast down the hill immediately. Instead you set the brake after getting it to the top of the hill. You could then come along at any later time, release the brake and get the ride you already paid for with muscular work. The work, or energy, must have remained in the wagon while it stood still at the crest of the hill.

This kind of stored-up energy of things at rest is called *potential energy*. The energy of any raised weight —the wagon at the top of the hill, an uplifted hammer, a boulder at the edge of a cliff, water at the top of a waterfall—is potential energy. If the boulder should topple over the cliff its potential energy would change to kinetic energy as it began to move faster and faster.

The boulder's stored-up energy becomes energy of motion.

As the boulder hit the ground this kinetic energy would be used up in breaking the boulder to pieces, in ramming it into the earth and in sending out sound waves through the air.

There are other forms of potential energy that do not make use of raised weights. How about the work you do in winding a watch? It is stored as potential energy in the watch spring, waiting to be used in setting the works into motion. A stick of dynamite looks like any piece of wood, but there is a great difference. Too bad if you find out about it by pounding on the stick! Dynamite contains a great amount of chemical potential energy. A wooden stick has a little of this kind of energy, too. To get it, we must let the stick burn. This gives off heat—a form of energy.

When you do work in order to give something mechanical energy, the original energy seems to have disappeared after everything is finished. A coaster wagon, given a strong shove, goes for a while but finally comes to rest. Pull back on a swing and let it go. You find that it swings back and forth a great many times. But each trip is a little shorter than the one before it, and soon the swing is standing still again. What becomes of the energy in such cases? The answer is that it does not really disappear, but changes into *heat*, which is another form of energy. The wheels of the wagon are a little warmer after a run than before. If you had a very delicate thermometer, you would find that the air is ever so slightly heated by the swishing of the swing through it.

It was not always known that heat could be produced by wasting away mechanical energy. In fact, only a hundred years ago scientists talked of heat as some kind of weightless fluid that could flow from one place to another. When a heated stone was placed in a bucket of water, they imagined that heat-fluid streamed out of the stone and went into the water, until everything reached the same temperature.

The person who first made clear the connection between mechanical energy and heat was an American named Benjamin Thompson, who lived at the time our country was getting her independence. This adventurous man was a scientific adviser to the Prince of Bavaria. One of his duties was to watch over the arsenal where guns and other weapons were made for the Bavarian army. Here huge cylinders of brass were bored out to make cannon. There were no electric motors in that day, nor even any practical steam engines. So the boring machine was powered by a horse walking a treadmill.

People had watched the making of cannon many times before. Most of them must have noticed that the tool and the chips of metal coming from it became very hot. Thompson's curiosity prompted him to do some experimenting to find out where the heat came from. He noticed that heat would keep coming out of the metal no matter how long the boring went on. This could not be the case if the heat-fluid idea were right because it would mean that each object would hold only a limited amount of this fluid.

"If I can *measure* the amount of heat, it may give me the clue," he said to himself. "Whip up your horse!"

he called to a workman. The animal strained forward on the treadmill, and chips of brass flew from the tool. Quickly Thompson scooped up a heap of the hot metal and dumped it into a pail of water. Then he stirred the water briskly with a big thermometer, scanning the mercury as it crept up the scale.

Several times the experiments were repeated. Between times, Thompson made calculations. At last one thing became clear to him: "The heating of the water seems to depend only on how much work is done by the horse. Yes, that is it—the work done by the horse is actually *changed into heat!*"

Thompson dumped the hot metal chips into a pail of water.

The old idea that heat was a fluid and that only a definite amount could be drained out of an object seemed open to question. Thompson's tests encouraged other people to work on the problem. Later, James Joule, an English brewer whose hobby was science, made careful experiments that backed up Thompson's ideas. Joule tried all sorts of ways to change mechanical energy into heat—by rubbing, by stirring water, by pounding a block of metal. Always, he found that to get a certain amount of heat, a definite amount of work (energy) was needed.

Measurements show that heat is expensive when paid for with work. If all the kinetic energy of a car moving 6o miles an hour were to change into heat, there would be only enough to boil a teakettle full of water. The change can go the other way around too. Heat is traded for mechanical energy in a steam engine or in a gas engine. This kind of change is harder to bring about and usually a great deal of the heat escapes in the process.

It remained for a young German physician named Robert Mayer to piece together the work of Thompson and Joule and come up with the great Energy Principle that *energy can be changed from one form to another, but it can never be created or destroyed.*

Although people did not believe in it at first, this principle has turned out to be one of the most important and useful of all scientific laws. It seems to rule everything that happens in the universe, from the wriggling of germs to the rushing of stars through space. Nobody has ever found an exception to it.

So you have seen that in the world around us there is *matter* and there is *energy*. Energy is something that gives life and activity to objects. It may take many different forms, but its total amount stays the same. In the following chapters you will get a closer look at matter and find out what it is made of.

CHAPTER 3

The Atom Idea Is Born

Atoms are nothing new. The word atom has become familiar to everybody only within the past few years, but the idea behind it goes back at least three thousand years. Of course nobody, not even the wisest men, had a definite idea of what atoms were. This came much later on. But at least a few people were beginning to observe Nature and to wonder how they might get a better understanding of what they saw.

The philosophers of ancient Greece had many a lively argument about the make-up of matter. One group said that it was obvious to think of any object as one solid piece, as it really appears to be. But other thinkers insisted that materials that seem solid and continuous must actually be made of countless tiny *particles* much too small to be seen. They discussed what would happen if any object were broken up. Suppose a stone is divided in two. Then one of the pieces is broken in two again, and so on. How far can this go? They believed that by continuing the breaking-up process they would eventually come down to the smallest particle of the material that could possibly exist. Such a particle they called an *atom*.

This idea of the Greek philosophers was probably not much more than a lucky guess. They did nothing to test their "hunch" by making experiments. If they had, they might have gotten much farther along the road to the truth. Little did they imagine that future scientists would not only be able to *prove* that atoms exist, but to find out how to weigh and measure them. The Greek philosophers would certainly have been astonished to know that if a single drop of water could be enlarged to the size of the earth, the atoms in it would appear only as big as basketballs. Or that the ink in the period at the end of this sentence is made up of about three million billion atoms of carbon. However, they did suspect one other thing that turned out, centuries later, to be correct: *The atoms are in constant motion.*

People continued to talk and argue about atoms for a few hundred years, but gradually the discussions began

Billions of atoms make up the ink in the period after a sentence.

to die out. It looked for a while as if this fine beginning were going to be lost. However, a good idea is hard to kill. The atomic theory, as it came to be called, was brought to life again about 150 years ago by an English schoolmaster named John Dalton.

Although he was extremely poor, Dalton managed to do scientific experiments by building his own instruments. One of his main interests was observing the weather and keeping daily records. This led him to think about how gases such as oxygen and nitrogen in the air might join up chemically with each other. His work marked the real start of the science of chemistry. But even more important for our story, it brought back the atom idea and put it on a firm basis.

For hundreds of years, experimenters had been tinkering with various kinds of substances. By long experience they began to learn that some materials would break down into new and different materials when "mistreated" in various ways—by pounding or by heating, for example. Suppose you want to find out what sugar is made of. Heat a spoonful of ordinary sugar over a flame, and you notice a crackling noise. At the same time, if you hold a knife blade over the sputtering sugar, a fog forms on it. The crackling sound and the appearance of moisture on the knife tell you that water has

Water comes out of the sugar and forms a fog on the knife.

come from the sugar. As the heating goes on, the sugar melts and darkens in color, finally becoming as black as coal. It is, actually, just that. Both coal and the black mess are carbon, which cannot be broken down into anything simpler.

What about the water that came out of the sugar? It turns out that this can be broken down further. At about the time of Dalton it was discovered that this could be done quite easily by connecting two wires to an electric battery and putting their ends into water. The electric current causes bubbles of oxygen gas to come from the water at one wire, and bubbles of hydrogen gas to come out at the other. Chemists have not been able to break either of these gases down into anything else.

Substances such as carbon, oxygen, hydrogen and about a hundred others that have been discovered are called chemical *elements*. All the many other materials we find in our surroundings—wood, stone, milk, rubber, salt and hundreds of thousands more—are made of combinations of these few elements. Such combinations are called chemical *compounds*.

It took years of patient work by scientists all over the world to discover and separate out the elements that we know. Some, such as silver, gold, tin and carbon, were known from ancient times; but people did not realize that they were elements—that they were "simpler" substances than salt or limestone or alcohol. Other elements have been discovered only in the last few years, and it is possible that still others may turn up.

Most of the hundred or so elements are quite rare and are not found in the common things around us. Nature seems to have added just a speck of them when the universe was made. Actually, the ordinary materials of the earth, sea and air are made up mainly of about thirty elements and their compounds. Here is a list of these elements. Alongside each name is the chemist's shorthand sign, or symbol, for each.

Some of the More Plentiful Chemical Elements

Name	Symbol	Description
Aluminum	Al	Lightweight silvery metal
Barium	Ba	Soft shiny metal
Bromine	Br	Heavy brown liquid
Calcium	Ca	Lightweight shiny metal
Carbon	C	Black solid, or clear crystals (diamond)
Chlorine	Cl	Greenish-yellow gas

Name	Symbol	Description
Cobalt	Co	Crumbly gray metal
Copper	Cu	Soft reddish metal
Fluorine	F	Light yellow gas
Gold	Au	Heavy, soft, yellow metal
Hydrogen	H	Lightweight invisible gas
Iodine	I	Dark purple crystals
Iron	Fe	Gray metal
Lead	Pb	Heavy, soft, blue-gray metal
Lithium	Li	Lightweight, soft, white metal
Magnesium	Mg	Lightweight white metal
Manganese	Mn	Crumbly, gray-white metal
Mercury	Hg	Heavy, silvery, liquid metal
Nickel	Ni	Hard white metal
Nitrogen	N	Invisible gas
Oxygen	O	Invisible gas
Phosphorus	P	Waxlike white solid
Potassium	K	Lightweight, soft, silvery metal
Silicon	Si	Crumbly gray crystals
Silver	Ag	Heavy, shiny white metal
Sodium	Na	Lightweight, soft, silvery metal
Sulfur	S	Light yellow, crumbly crystals
Tin	Sn	Silvery white metal
Titanium	Ti	Shiny white metal
Zinc	Zn	Crumbly, blue-white metal

Sodium (a metal) and chlorine (a gas) are combined to form salt.

Most likely you have never seen a great many of these elements. This is because they are usually locked up in compounds where they lose their identity. For instance, sodium is a shiny metal and chlorine is a gas with an irritating smell, yet you sprinkle a compound of them on your food every day. Chemists call this compound sodium chloride; you know it as table salt. You might never guess that the white salt crystals have the metal and the greenish gas mysteriously hidden in them.

Oxygen is by far the most plentiful element on earth, not only because it is found in air and water, but because it is part of so many compounds in rocks and minerals. Very often it is combined with silicon, as in quartz and some kinds of sand. Oxygen and silicon and aluminum find themselves together in such materials as clay. These three elements, in their compounds, make up over three-quarters of the earth's solid crust.

Now you are ready to see what Dalton did to push ahead our knowledge of atoms. He decided to see *how much* of each element is needed to form its compounds. By experimenting with many elements, he found that he could always *mix* two or more of them in any amounts he pleased. But if he wanted to form an actual compound, they had to be used only in a *certain proportion*. If he started with the elements in any different proportion, some was bound to be left over afterward.

John Dalton wondered why Nature was so particular about the amounts of materials that can join chemically. Most people would be satisfied to say, "It's true just because Nature made it that way." But Dalton, like the good scientist he was, wanted to go deeper into the question. He would not rest until he could find some logical plan that would tie together what he noticed in hundreds of cases where elements combined.

Scientists are always looking for general rules that connect and relate things. They feel that if they can find a simple idea that covers many separate things they have seen and noted, they have a better understanding of what is going on. Such an idea is called a scientific *theory*. Do not think, as some people carelessly do, that a theory is a fantastic vision that anyone can dream up; it most certainly is not. A good theory must be based on solid facts. Once it becomes established, it can serve as a faithful guide for leading science on to new discoveries.

Dalton took the atom idea of the ancient Greeks and made it more definite. "Suppose," he said to himself, "that each chemical element is made up of atoms. And imagine that the atoms of one element, such as hydrogen, are all *alike*, but different from the atoms of any other element, such as oxygen." He went on to suggest that the atoms of the various elements have different weights. When two elements combine chemically, a definite number of atoms of the first element always join up with a definite number of the other to form what is called a *molecule* of the compound. The hooked-together atoms keep the same weights they had when they were still separate.

This explains why elements always combine in definite proportions. For example, here is the way it works out for water, which is a compound of oxygen and hydrogen. If you mix these two gases in a strong tank and shoot a spark through the mixture, there will be a powerful explosion and water will form. If for every ounce of hydrogen there were originally eight ounces of oxygen, then you would find that everything joined up nicely, with neither any hydrogen nor any oxygen left over. But if you had put in more of one of these gases, some of that gas would remain, uncombined, after the explosion was over.

This kind of information tells chemists how the molecules of various compounds are made up. A story may help explain how this works out: Suppose a fruit dealer makes up packages containing grapefruit and plums. All the packages are exactly alike. The man tells us that each plum weighs one ounce and each grapefruit weighs 16 ounces. At the end of the day, he finds that all the grapefruit he has used weigh exactly 8 times as much as all the plums. Can you tell from this how much of each kind of

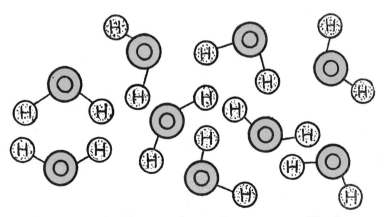

Every water molecule is made up of two atoms of hydrogen joined to one atom of oxygen.

fruit was put into each package? The answer is that there must be two plums and one grapefruit in each package.

In this story, a plum stands for a hydrogen atom and a grapefruit stands for an oxygen atom. Each complete package represents a molecule of water. Chemists know that an oxygen atom weighs 16 times as much as a hydrogen atom, and that one pound of hydrogen will combine with exactly 8 pounds of oxygen to form water. This tells them that there must be *two* atoms of hydrogen to each atom of oxygen in every molecule of water, just as there had to be two plums to each grapefruit in a package.

And it goes the same way when a compound is broken down into its elements. When water is separated into its elements, eight ounces of oxygen always come out for each ounce of hydrogen. Whether we start with a drop or a gallon, the proportion is always the same.

The atom idea maps things out clearly. It tells us that all materials are made of atoms and molecules, just as our language is made up of hundreds of thousands of words which are all combinations of just the twenty-six letters of the alphabet.

The atomic theory was quickly taken up by many scientists who recognized its great value in helping to put chemistry on a firm basis. Progress became rapid. Only about twenty elements were known to Dalton. Less than fifty years later this number had grown to seventy-five. The atom was becoming something real, even though nobody had ever seen one!

From their experiments with many compounds, chemists worked out a list of numbers that stand for the weights of atoms of the elements. These are called *atomic weights*. For convenience, oxygen was given the number 16, and all the other atomic weights were measured up and down from this point. Starting with hydrogen, the lightest kind of atom, here are the exact values for the first dozen elements:

Atomic Weights of Some of the Elements

Name	Symbol	Atomic Weight
Hydrogen	H	1.008
Helium	He	4.003
Lithium	Li	6.940
Beryllium	Be	9.015
Boron	B	10.82
Carbon	C	12.01
Nitrogen	N	14.01
Oxygen	O	16.00

Name	Symbol	Atomic Weight
Fluorine	F	19.00
Neon	Ne	20.18
Sodium	Na	23.00
Magnesium	Mg	24.32

These numbers do not mean, for example, that a single atom of hydrogen weighs about one pound, or even one ounce. Actually, there are over a quarter of a billion billion billion atoms to a pound of hydrogen. The figures mean only that a hydrogen atom is about one-sixteenth as heavy as one of oxygen, that a neon atom is about 20 times the weight of a hydrogen atom, and so on.

But there was a great deal of work ahead. Scientists still knew nothing about the actual size of atoms, nor how they moved—if at all. This and much more knowledge was to come in the years that followed.

CHAPTER 4

Are Atoms Real?

Up to Dalton's time the atom idea was mainly of interest to chemists, who were slowly working their way toward proving that atoms exist. They were trying to find out how materials *differ* from each other. But even before this, some scientists had begun to discover that there were general rules telling how all kinds of matter acted in the *same* way. These scientists studied all forms of energy, including light and electricity. The studies were enough different from chemistry to form a separate branch of science called *physics*, and the people working on these problems came to be known as *physicists*.

More than a hundred years before Dalton's time, the great Isaac Newton worked out the idea of *gravitation* —the mysterious force that makes a stone fall to the ground and that holds the earth and other planets in their paths around the sun. Newton also wondered whether any other kind of force was at work among the molecules of matter. He believed that air or any other gas presses against the sides of its container because of some force that pushes the molecules away from each other, like rubber balls jammed tightly into a box.

But not all scientists agreed. Some wanted to go back to the ancient Greek idea that atoms are constantly *moving*. They suggested that the reason for gas pressure is not that the molecules are squeezed together but that they are in motion. They pictured a gas in a bottle as a swarm of tiny particles that are constantly flying about, bumping into each other and into the sides of the bottle. Because there are so many molecules doing this, the effect is like a steady push.

In order to see where this idea led them, think of a simple hand pump that boys use to inflate a football or bicycle tire. This is really a machine for compressing air, forcing it into a smaller space. The air inside a bicycle tire takes up less than half as much room as it did when outside. In pumping up the tire you notice that the farther you push the handle down, the harder it pushes

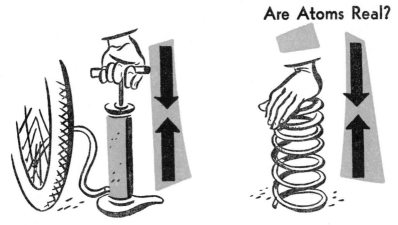

The farther you push down, the harder it pushes back.

back on your hand. When squeezed into a smaller space, air acts like a spring ready to push back.

Next, imagine that the outlet hose of the pump is plugged up. When the handle is pushed down, the air has no place to go and so is packed tighter in the bottom of the pump itself. The moving molecules now hit the sides of their container more often because they no longer have so far to travel. More hits mean more pressure.

A young Irish scientist named Robert Boyle, who lived during Newton's time, discovered that when a gas is forced into half its former space, its pressure exactly doubles. If it is packed into one-third the space, the pressure gets three times as big, and so on. It began to seem clear that when you compress a gas you do not squeeze together some sort of rubber-like substance as

33

All About the Atom

Newton believed. Instead, you simply cut down the "elbow room" of the tiny, swift-moving molecules.

Boyle's discovery led to many new ideas. Scientists imagined a bottle filled with gas to be like a room in which many never-resting tennis balls were flying about. Calculations were made. It turned out that merely by knowing the pressure and weight of the gas they could figure out how fast its molecules were moving. For molecules of oxygen and nitrogen in the air, the average speed comes to about 1,700 feet a second—twice the speed of a bullet from a "22" rifle. And for hydrogen, which is much lighter, the speed comes out nearly four times as great.

At that time nobody dared to believe that anything could move this fast, and for a long while even physicists refused to take the idea seriously. After all, had anyone ever *seen* these moving molecules? Not quite. But an English botanist named Robert Brown had seen the next best thing. He was using a microscope to look at some tiny plant cells floating in water. To his surprise, the cells kept dancing around with a peculiar trembling movement. The puzzling thing about all this darting and wiggling was that it never stopped.

Brown was unable to account for what he discovered,

and it was not until many years later that others found an explanation, using the fact that the molecules of a liquid, like those of a gas, are in swift motion. When the plant cells are hit from all sides by water molecules, they jump around. This action was named the *Brownian motion*, after its discoverer. It is the nearest we have come to seeing the actual movement of molecules. So, while the molecules themselves are invisible, the effect of their movement is plainly seen.

At last physicists were in a position to understand some of the effects they had noticed when experimenting with gases, liquids and solids. Most important of all, they began to realize that *the kinetic energy of the helter-skelter motion of the molecules is the same thing as heat*. When you warm something, you are really giving more energy of movement to its molecules. If you accidentally touch a hot stove, the fast moving molecules of the hot metal actually pound on the molecules of your skin.

A bullet flying through the air has kinetic energy, and it is clear that something is moving. After the bullet stops in the target, the motion is still there, but is no longer visible because it has all been changed into motion of the molecules, which is *heat*.

If all the heat-motion could be taken away from the molecules of an object, it would reach a temperature called *absolute zero*. This is about 460 degrees below zero of the ordinary thermometer scale. During the past few years, experimenters have found ways to chill substances to within a few thousandths of a degree of this point. But nothing has actually reached it.

Gradually scientists began to piece together an idea of how matter is built up out of molecules. They now understand that in a solid, the atoms and molecules cling together in some regular kind of arrangement, stacked in even rows running in certain directions. The rows

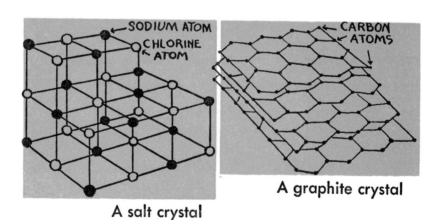

A salt crystal

A graphite crystal

In a solid, molecules and atoms cling together in some kind of regular arrangement.

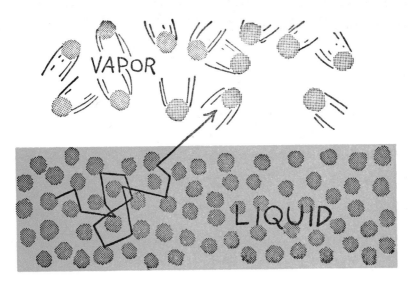

Molecules that get away from a liquid become the vapor.

are usually not much more than a hundred-millionth of an inch apart. Such an arrangement is called a *crystal*. In a salt crystal, the sodium atoms and the chlorine atoms hold each other in place at the corners of an imaginary cubical framework. In a crystal of graphite, the carbon atoms are lined up in six-sided figures, one layer above another.

But do not think that the atoms are standing still— each one has its fast, trembling heat-motion. If the crystal is warmed, the movement increases until, at a certain temperature, the atoms break away from each other and the solid *melts*. Now the material is liquid, and the atoms or molecules are free to slide around. Since the molecules are bumping into each other all the time, there will be some, now and then, that get up to a much higher speed than most of the others. If one of these speedier molecules happens to come near the surface of the liquid, it may escape altogether. This is called *evaporation*. The molecules that get away from the liquid become the vapor, which is a *gas*.

The spreading of one gas through another gives a good way of picturing how the moving molecules act. If you take the stopper out of a bottle of perfume, the liquid begins to evaporate into the air; but it takes some time before the scent gets to the opposite side of the room. If it were not for the air in the room, the perfume molecules, traveling hundreds of feet a second, would reach the far side in no time at all. But in order to get across, they have to fight their way through a tremendous crowd of air molecules.

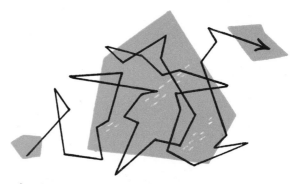

The path of an individual vapor molecule is a zigzag one.

A vapor molecule finds it can go only a very short distance before it bumps into an air molecule, which may send it off in some quite different direction. As a result, the path of an individual vapor molecule must be a wild, zigzag one, very much like the path of one of the little solid particles in the Brownian motion mentioned earlier. A gas, such as air, is mostly empty space, with molecules scattered through it. But because the molecules are moving, they occupy the whole space, keeping other things out, in the same way that soldiers occupy a captured country.

It was only about forty or fifty years ago that physicists were able to work out this idea to the point where they could count molecules and measure their sizes and weights. Of course, when we say "measure" we mean something very indirect. For it is still true that nobody has actually *seen* a single atom or molecule, even though science has been able to get a hazy sort of shadow picture of some of the larger molecules by using x-rays or the electron microscope.

Even though molecules remain unseen, they leave enough clues from which physicists can figure out such definite things as weight and size. Since the same answers come out from very different kinds of evidence, it

If a grain of salt were as big as the Empire State Building,
each atom within that grain would be only a tiny dot.

would be impossible for the whole idea of molecules to be wrong. To a physicist, a molecule exists as certainly as the chair he sits on.

Some of the results are truly astonishing—if we can grasp them at all. Atoms and molecules are unbelievably small. Eighty million oxygen molecules, placed in a row like marbles, would stretch a distance of only an inch.

If you could magnify a single grain of table salt until it became as big as the Empire State Building, each atom in it would look only about as big as the grain you started with.

An English scientist once told a story that may help you realize how many molecules there are in ordinary things. Fill a drinking glass with water. Suppose you had some way of marking each water molecule so you could recognize it if you saw it again. Now pour the water down the drain. Wait a long, long time until this water has had a chance to mix with all the oceans of the earth. Then go down to the seashore anywhere in the world and scoop up a glassful of water. Do you suppose there is a chance that any of the original marked molecules will be in it? The answer is that the glass will contain over a *thousand* of them!

There is more to the story of the unseen molecules. A molecule in the air bumps into other molecules about five billion times a second. Knowing about how fast they move, you can figure out that, on the average, an air molecule goes only a few millionths of an inch before it hits another one. Perhaps you have wondered why, with all this bumping, the molecules of the air never "settle out" on the floor and come to rest, like tennis balls thrown at the walls of a room. Nowadays scientists know that these collisions are not the actual bumping-together of hard objects. Instead, as the molecules come very close together, they push each other away with strong electrical forces, so no energy is wasted and the movement never dies out.

The things that happen in the fantastic world of molecules sometimes sound like the wildest science fiction, but they are tested and true beyond any doubt. These facts paved the way for even more wonderful discoveries that came swiftly, one after another, during the last fifty years or so.

CHAPTER 5

Smaller Than an Atom

One of the next things to do in getting ready to learn about atoms is to comb your hair! A comb that has been drawn briskly through your hair several times will attract small bits of paper to it. In dry weather, you may hear a slight crackling sound as you comb, and in the dark you can even see tiny sparks. This is truly thunder and lightning on a small scale.

In ancient Greece, people had already noticed such things. They found that when a piece of amber was rubbed with fur, it mysteriously pulled little bits of wood toward it, making them dance about in a very odd way. Not much more was discovered for many centuries. At about the time the Pilgrims were getting ready to leave for the New World, British scientists noticed that many other materials besides amber would attract. Even though they were not sure what caused this pulling power, they gave it a name: *electricity*, after the Greek word for amber.

They found out much more, and you can check some of these results yourself by making a little detector of electricity called an *electroscope*. Take a well-dried potato and cut out a ball about half an inch across. Cover the ball with a layer of thin metal foil (chewing gum wrapper, for instance) and hang it up by a piece of silk thread about two feet long. Run the comb through your hair a few times and bring it toward the ball. As the comb comes within a few inches, the ball begins to swing toward it.

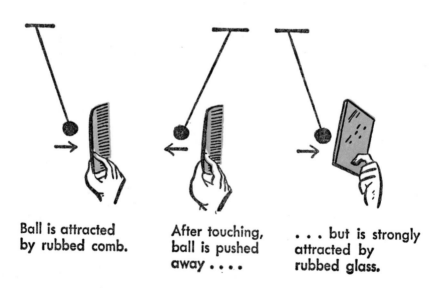

Ball is attracted by rubbed comb.

After touching, ball is pushed away . . . .

. . . but is strongly attracted by rubbed glass.

If by chance the two touch, something new happens. The ball immediately pushes *away* from the comb, and bringing the comb closer only makes the ball back off. This shows something very important. In electricity there are forces pushing things apart as well as forces pulling things together.

Rub a piece of clean glass with a silk cloth. When you bring the glass near the ball, the two attract each other. Touch the ball with your finger. This removes all effects, leaving the ball just as it was at the start.

Now repeat everything, but wherever you used the comb before, use the glass. And wherever you used the glass in the first experiment, use the comb. The results will be exactly as before.

Each time you touched the ball with the rubbed comb or glass you gave it an electrical *charge*. What happened in the experiments can be explained by the fact that there are two *opposite* kinds of electrical charge. Our own Benjamin Franklin suggested that we keep things straight by naming the two kinds *positive* (+) and *negative* (−). Rubbing certain materials such as glass gives them a + charge. Others, such as plastic, get a − charge when rubbed.

Everything can be summed up by saying, "Charges of the same kind push each other apart, while charges of opposite kind attract." This means that a pair of + charged objects will shove each other apart, and so will a pair of − charges, but a + and a − will attract each other. There we have the whole thing in a neat rule.

Benjamin Franklin, with his famous kite experiment, showed that lightning is nothing but a huge electric spark. Before long, others were discovering how to put electricity to work. Eventually scientists and engineers found that when electricity is controlled and made to move along wires, it can do many useful tasks—run

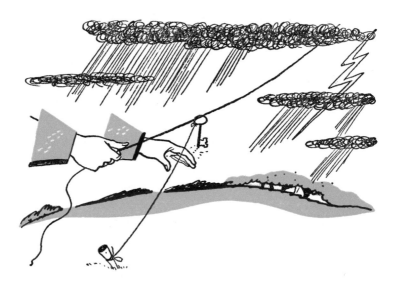

Ben Franklin showed that lightning is just a big electric spark.

In the tube the spark became a soft, silent glow.

motors, operate telephones, light buildings. Electricity makes possible such modern miracles as radio, radar and television, all from the simple experiments that began when someone first rubbed a piece of amber.

A hundred years ago, scientists were justly proud of what they had already found out about atoms, molecules and electricity, but they did not realize how closely connected these subjects are. The next big step came when they found a better method of getting molecules out of their way in certain experiments.

If a high enough electrical voltage is put on an object, a spark will jump across through the air to something else near by. In every way this is the same as a lightning flash that leaps between clouds, or between a cloud and the earth, during a storm.

In order to find out more about what happens, physicists put the spark in a glass tube like the one in the picture. By this time, good vacuum pumps had been perfected, so the experimenters were able to pump out the tube and find out what went on at lower pressures. When they got rid of some of the air molecules inside the tube, the spark changed greatly in appearance. As the pumping went on, the sharp, crackling spark gave way to a soft, silent glow. When less than a hundredth of the air was left, the glow filled nearly the whole tube and cast a strong, pinkish light in all directions. This is no different from the familiar "neon" signs that we see everywhere, except that they usually contain neon gas, mercury vapor or certain other gases instead of air.

Very complicated things are happening in such a tube. The molecules of the gas help carry electric charges back and forth between the metal disks. If still more of the air is pumped out, the glow finally fades away, since there are no longer enough molecules to carry the current. By the time the pump has pulled out all but about 1/100,000 of the air, the space between the disks no longer lights up at all, but the sides of the glass tube now begin to shine with a blue-green glow.

The glow comes only from the parts of the glass that are opposite the negative plate. It seems to be caused by rays that shoot out of this plate in straight lines. What can they be? There are two possibilities. They might be

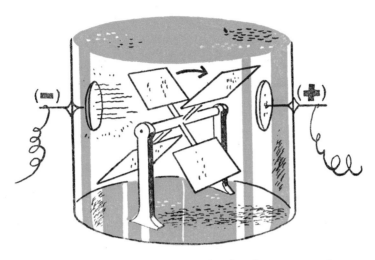

When rays hit the paddle wheel, it began to spin.

light rays of some kind, or else streams of particles. The experimenters set to work to find out which idea was right. One scientist set up a tiny paddle wheel inside the vacuum tube and found that it would spin when the rays hit it. This certainly was in favor of the particle idea.

Other experimenters discovered that when a magnet was brought near the tube, the rays would bend to one side. This proved that the particles carried electric charges, because it was already known that a stream of moving charges is pushed aside by a magnet. This really ruled out any idea that the rays were like light, because you know that it is impossible to bend a beam of light from your flashlight by putting a magnet next to it. So here, not much more than fifty years ago when most scientists thought that everything important had already been discovered, they were faced with something entirely new. What were these mysterious charged particles? And what, if anything, did they have to do with atoms?

The answer was given by the experiments of Professor Joseph John Thomson of Cambridge University in England, who lived until just before World War II. After carefully checking the earlier work of other scientists, he went on to find that the rays could be swerved aside by electrical forces as well as by magnets. Then he built a vacuum tube in which the rays could be bent either by magnet coils or by electrically-charged metal plates. He figured out that this would tell him something more about the particles that made up these puzzling rays.

The surprising result was that the particles were all alike. They would all hit exactly the same spot on the end of the tube, regardless of what kind of metal was used to make the disk they came out of, or what kind of gas was in the tube to begin with. If the particles had been of different kinds, they would have spread out because the lighter ones would be pushed aside more than the heavier ones. In every case, here were particles all having the same weight and each carrying the same-sized bit of negative electric charge. The particles were named *electrons*.

The hardest thing of all to believe was that the weight of an electron turned out to be over a thousand times smaller than the weight of even the lightest atom—hydrogen. Most physicists refused to have anything to do with the electron idea. Thomson himself began to have doubts.

But no—it was true. Other workers measured the charge of electricity that the electron carried. They found it unbelievably small. We now know that the current that lights your desk lamp is made up of a swarm of electrons struggling along among the atoms of the copper wire. Electrons are so small that more than three billion billion must go through the lamp each second in order to light it.

As time went on, many ways were found to make electrons come out of all sorts of materials. They can be pulled out by strong electrical forces, as in vacuum tubes. They can be knocked out by fast particles, or they can be "boiled out" of a hot wire. They can be shaken out of a piece of metal by means of light waves. No matter which way we get them loose, they are always exactly alike. And because they are so much lighter and smaller than any atom, scientists had to admit that *electrons must be part of the atoms themselves.*

And what about the old idea that atoms cannot be broken down into anything simpler? From here on, this had to be thought of in a new way because now it was clear that atoms must be made up of still smaller things. Electrons make up one part. Was there anything else? There had to be, for it was hard to think of atoms having only negative electricity in them. The simplest thing would be to imagine that each atom contains just enough positive electricity to balance out the negative charge of the electrons in it. And this turned out to be true.

CHAPTER 6

Some Atoms Break Down

Now the story goes back to just before World War I. A crowd of important personages fills the State Ballroom at Buckingham Palace in London. At one end of the huge room the King sits upon a raised platform. A line of men moves slowly down the aisle. One by one they approach the King until it is the turn of a tall, husky man to come forward. He bows, then kneels before the throne. An attendant hands the King a ceremonial sword, and the King touches the kneeling figure with it on each shoulder, saying, "Rise, Sir Ernest."

From a balcony, a slight, gray-haired lady views the ceremony. She is tired from her long journey from far-off Australia but she watches eagerly, and there is a proud smile on her face. For this is her son, Ernest Rutherford, the farm boy who became a great scientific genius. Now he was being given one of the highest honors a grateful nation could grant.

At the age of 24, Rutherford had come from his homeland to study physics in Thomson's laboratory. The young scientist showed much talent, and soon he was working on his own experiments. The year was 1898, the time of the Spanish-American War.

At about this time, it was found that a material containing the element uranium gave off radiation that could go through ordinary materials. Pierre and Marie Curie set to work to find out what these unusual rays were

Pierre and Marie Curie discovered several new chemical elements.

and where they came from. Everyone knows the story of how they labored for years until they finally discovered several new chemical elements. Among these was radium, which turned out to be millions of times more active than uranium.

Further experiments turned up still other *radioactive* elements. Of course, the word has no connection with the "radio" that we listen to. It means that the atoms of these elements continually give off rays of some kind.

What *was* this radiation? Science had to know. Ernest Rutherford found part of the answer. Some of the rays are strong, but cannot travel far—a sheet of paper stops them completely. Rutherford called these *alpha rays*. Others were found that have less energy, but are able to go about a hundred times as far. These he called *beta* rays. Before long, a third part of the radiation was discovered. These rays proved to be far more penetrating than either of the others, for they could go through a thick stone wall. They were named *gamma rays*. Alpha, beta and gamma are the first three letters of the Greek alphabet. (The word "alphabet" comes from the first two, as you see.)

Rutherford and the men who worked with him were able to trace down the character of each of these rays from several radioactive elements. The clue was that alphas and betas could be swerved aside by electrical or magnetic forces, just like the electrons in Thomson's experiments. The gamma rays could not be bent at all, which showed that they were like light waves. They turned out to be similar to x-rays, but much more penetrating, and were found to be useful in treating cancer.

From the directions in which the alphas and betas curved, the experimenters knew that alphas were streams of positive particles, while betas were streams of negatives. It did not take long to prove that beta particles were really electrons. Instead of getting their kinetic energy in a vacuum tube, they are shot out naturally by the atoms of various radioactive materials.

Alphas could be bent aside only very slightly, which showed that they are much heavier particles. The alpha particle turned out to be an *atom of helium* from which two electrons had been removed. How these alphas were produced when an atom of radium blew itself to pieces was still a big mystery. Since each alpha lacked two electrons, it really carried two positive charges, because *taking away negatives* from a normal atom with balanced pairs of + and − charges is the same thing as *adding positives* to it. The scientific sign, or symbol, for

When a helium atom throws off two electrons, it becomes He^{++}.

an alpha particle is He^{++}, showing that it is an atom of the element helium carrying two positive charges of electricity. Next to hydrogen, helium is the lightest element known to chemists.

The atoms of radium and about ten other heavy elements are continually shooting out electrons and alpha particles. And the terrific speeds of the particles gave scientists the first hint of the great amounts of energy that must be locked up inside. Searching into an atom is like opening up a seemingly empty box only to find that it contains many interesting and unusual treasures.

In spite of the new discoveries, things were becoming harder to understand. What else might there be in an atom besides alpha and beta particles? Later, two other particles were found. One of these is the *proton*, which is a hydrogen atom with one electron removed. Its symbol is H$^+$. The other is the *neutron*, which has almost exactly the same weight as a proton but has no electrical charge. It is electrically *neutral*. It was found that an alpha particle is really a cluster of two protons and two neutrons that, for some reason, stick tightly together.

Here is a table showing the most important facts about these particles:

The Particles That Make Up Atoms

Name	Symbol	Weight (Weight of electron is called 1)	Electrical Charge (Electron charge is −1)
Electron	e	1	−1
Proton	H^+	1,836	+1
Neutron	n	1,838	0
Alpha particle	He^{++}	7,300	+2

Beta particle   (fast electron shot out of a radioactive atom)

One of Rutherford's fellow scientists had come upon a simple and clever way of watching radioactive atoms break down. He found that when an alpha particle hits a material like the coating on a TV screen, there is a tiny flash of light. You can see this very thing happening right at home! All you need is a watch or clock with a luminous dial. Rest your eyes in a perfectly dark room for a few minutes, then look at the figures on the dial

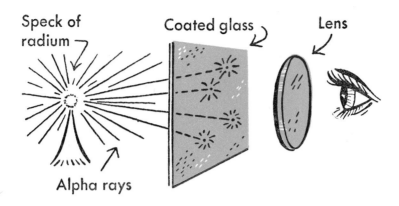

Speck of radium

Coated glass

Lens

Alpha rays

Each flash is caused by an alpha particle shooting out.

with a fairly strong magnifying lens. In place of the steady glow, you will see countless flickering points of light. Each flash is caused by an alpha particle shot out from a radium atom and striking the coating on the dial.

Rutherford fixed up an alpha counter based on this idea. He placed a tiny speck of radioactive material near a coated piece of glass and mounted a lens behind this. Every time a radium atom breaks down, an alpha shoots out, so counting alphas told him how fast the radium was breaking down. It does not actually disappear, but changes into another chemical element. This in turn breaks down into still another kind of atom, and so on.

These changes were tracked down in Rutherford's laboratory for many radioactive substances. In every case, after going through several changes, sometimes shooting out an alpha, sometimes a beta, the radioactive atom ended up as an atom of lead.

Using the flash counter, the experimenters found that radioactive elements break down in a peculiar way. The more material you have on hand, the faster it is disappearing. The drawing shows how this goes. Suppose you start with exactly one ounce of a certain radioactive element. Imagine that after one hour, you find its activity to be only half as great as before, which means that just half the original amount is left. Then after another hour, you would find that half of this quantity, or ¼ ounce, is left. Wait another hour and ⅛ is left. After still another hour, only ¹⁄₁₆ ounce would remain, and so on.

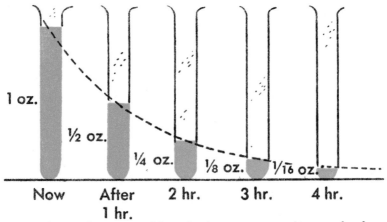

1 oz.

½ oz.

¼ oz.   ⅛ oz.   ¹⁄₁₆ oz.

Now   After   2 hr.   3 hr.   4 hr.
          1 hr.

Every hour, the material breaks down more and more slowly.

This is the way it goes for every active element. The material keeps on breaking down, but more and more slowly as time goes on. Think of a tree that begins to lose its leaves in the autumn. At first when almost all the leaves are still on the tree, very many are seen to fall to the ground every minute. As time goes on, the number remaining becomes much less and so does the number dropping off each minute.

In the example shown in the drawing, one hour was the time needed for half the amount to disappear. This period of time is called the *half-life* of the element. Depending on the material, it may be anywhere from less than a millionth of a second to over a hundred billion years.

Radium has a half-life of about 1,560 years. Suppose an Egyptian king had sealed up an ounce of radium in one of the pyramids when it was built nearly 4,700 years ago. After 1,560 years, only half an ounce would be left, and after another 1,560 years only one-fourth. After still another 1,560 years (which brings us to the present time) only an eighth of an ounce of radium would remain.

Nothing we can do to any radioactive material has the slightest effect on the way it breaks down. Heating or cooling it, shining light on it, passing electricity through it—none of these things can change the speed at which it wastes away. Radioactivity seems to be Nature's clock that has been ticking away in perfect time ever since the world began.

And all the while, energy is being given out in the form of gamma rays and as kinetic energy of the alpha and beta particles. A single ounce of radium gives off as much energy as the burning of ten tons of coal. This is true "atomic energy," and scientists knew about it more than 50 years ago. But radium and other radioactive elements were so scarce that nobody dreamed of putting this kind of energy to practical use.

CHAPTER 7

Mapping the Atoms

Suppose you were to stretch a sheet of tissue paper across a hoop, set it up in the back yard and throw base- balls at it. The very first ball to hit the paper would rip through and keep right on going. Put a fresh piece of paper on the hoop and try once more. Every ball that hits will go through, and this happens again and again. But just as you are beginning to lose interest in this game you decide to throw one more ball. You watch it speed toward the hoop, waiting to hear the ripping sound of the paper. But the ball does not go through— it bounces off the paper and comes back toward you! Hard to believe? Yet this is just what Rutherford found happening to alpha particles in his next great experiment.

In this work, the baseballs were alpha particles shot out of radium at nearly 10,000 miles a second. The tissue paper was a sheet of gold leaf a hundred times thinner than a piece of paper. Most of the alpha particles went straight on through the gold foil. Being so tiny, they naturally left no visible holes. But some of the alphas were swung to the side by different amounts, and a few even bounced straight back in the direction from which they came.

From other information, Rutherford was able to figure out that most of the alpha particles had to go *right through the atoms* of the gold leaf instead of *between* them. This must mean that an atom does not look very solid to a fast alpha particle, but has large open spaces through which the speeding particles can pass. Rutherford was puzzled. Here was something that sounded more like a magician's trick than a scientific experiment. He could see only one answer. These alphas do not actually bounce off the atoms of the metal foil but are turned aside by electrical forces. You recall that an alpha particle carries a positive charge. Then, by supposing that an atom has a positive charge at its center, we can explain everything as the pushing-apart of two positive charges. The alphas that pass some distance from the center of the atom are pushed aside only a little, but the ones that happen to graze close to the

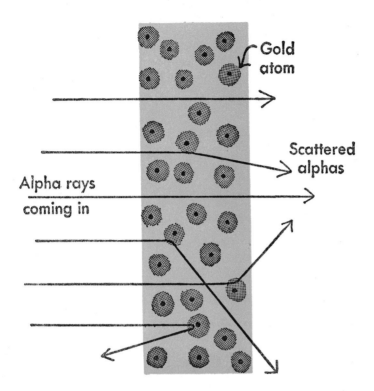

Gold atom

Scattered alphas

Alpha rays coming in

An atom has open spaces through which particles can pass.

center are swung off far to the side or even turned back.

The flash counter, described on page 59, was used to find out just how many of the alphas were thrown off in different directions. Summing up these results, Rutherford realized that the plus-charged center of the atom was not over a ten-millionth of a millionth of an inch across! This central core of an atom is called its *nucleus*. (The plural is *nuclei*.)

All About the Atom

When you remember that a whole atom is about one hundred-millionth of an inch wide, you realize that the nucleus must be a hundred thousand times smaller than the atom itself. If an atom were blown up to the size of a football stadium, the nucleus would be the size of a "B-B" shot placed on the 50-yard line.

A complete atom must be electrically neutral, so in order to balance the positive charge on the nucleus, there must be the proper number of negative-charged electrons somewhere else in the atom. Because the negative electrons are not pulled into the nucleus by its positive charge, Rutherford had to suppose that the electrons were whirling around the nucleus like planets circling around the sun, or like insects buzzing around a lamp on a summer evening. Then the force trying to make the electrons fly outward from the center balances out the electrical pull of the nucleus, and everything remains in order.

The electrons guard the outside of the atom. They act as a shield, keeping other atoms from coming too near. Only a swift, penetrating "bullet" such as an alpha particle can get by and come close to the nucleus.

Now the general layout of the atom becomes clear. In the center there is a heavy, tightly-packed nucleus.

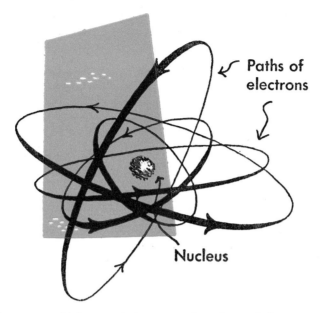

Paths of electrons

Nucleus

Electrons whirl around the central nucleus of the atom.

Far out, forming the boundary of the atom, is the shield of whirling electrons. This simple description makes it seem as if the atoms of all chemical elements are alike, but this is not true. Every atom, regardless of which chemical element it belongs to, is built on this general plan. But the nucleus and the number of outer electrons are different from one element to another.

Here are some examples of how atoms are built. An atom of hydrogen, the lightest element, has just a single proton for its nucleus. Outside, there is one electron, as the drawing shows. This is the simplest possible atom we can imagine. The next heavier element is helium. Chemists find that a helium atom is about four times as heavy as a hydrogen atom. This must mean that the helium nucleus itself is about four times as heavy as the hydrogen nucleus, because the outer electrons are too light to count much toward the total weight of the atom.

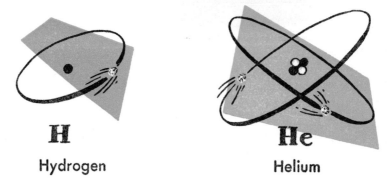

H

Hydrogen

He

Helium

The helium atom (right) is about four times as heavy as the hydrogen atom (left).

It is also known that no more than *two* electrons can ever be removed from a helium atom. This shows that the nucleus must have two plus charges if it is to hold on to these two outer electrons. In order for this nucleus to weigh about as much as four protons or neutrons, and at the same time have a charge of $+2$, it must be made up of *two protons and two neutrons*. So the helium nucleus must be just this combination.

Lithium, the next heavier atom, has three outer electrons. Its nucleus is about seven times as heavy as either the proton or neutron. To make the charge right, there must be three protons in the nucleus. The other four heavy particles that are needed must be neutrons.

By continuing to play this game, physicists were able to work out the plan of each of the other atoms. Uranium, the heaviest and most complicated atom found on earth, has a nucleus containing 92 protons and 146 neutrons, and there are 92 electrons swirling around outside.

In this way, the physicist was able to give the chemist a picture, or at least a rough map, of the atom of each element. All these hard-won facts about the parts of the atom greatly simplified things. Before this, scientists had to deal with over 90 different substances—the elements. As far as they knew, each one was really something quite different from the others. Now it became clear that there were only three different kinds of particles— protons, neutrons and electrons—the building blocks from which atoms of all kinds are made. We could hardly ask for anything neater.

CHAPTER 8

Different on the Inside

It seems to be a peculiar thing about the history of science that no sooner do some things get cleared up than new puzzles appear. Even before Rutherford had sketched the first rough maps of the atom, difficulties turned up.

In Chapter 5 you read about Thomson's experiments with a vacuum tube, in which he was able to turn electrons aside with a magnet. Having succeeded in finding out about electrons by this method, Thomson decided to build a vacuum tube in which he could do the same thing for positively-charged atoms. The high electrical voltage in such a tube knocks one or more electrons off the atoms of any gas that is left. This leaves these atoms with a positive charge, and so they begin to speed up in the opposite direction, rushed along by the electrical forces.

The experiment is very much like the one with electrons. But here, with several different elements in the tube, there are charged atoms of various weights. Instead of all following the same path, they bend by different amounts, the lighter ones more than the heavier ones.

The picture shows what happens. Each kind of atom follows a separate path, landing finally on a photographic film where it makes a spot. From the position of a spot, the experimenter can tell the exact weight of the atoms that caused it. The whole thing is really an arrangement that sorts out individual atoms according to their weight.

One of the first things Thomson did with his new setup was to try to weigh atoms of neon gas. According

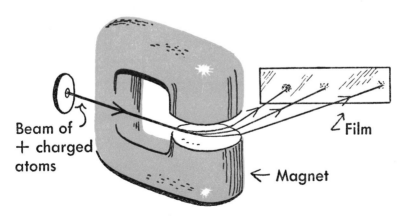

Beam of
+ charged
atoms

Film

← Magnet

Each kind of atom follows a separate path to the film.

to the chemists' table on page 30, a neon atom should have a weight of 20.18. However, when the film was developed, *two* spots were found—one at 20 and a fainter one at 22. "It must be," said Thomson, "that there really are *two* kinds of neon atoms, one with a weight of 20 and another with a weight of 22. The neon that we find in our surroundings is merely a mixture of these two kinds, with an average weight of 20.18." Chemically, both kinds act exactly alike, and there is no way to tell one from another. But a device like Thomson's atom sorter could separate them because of their slight difference in weight.

Having made this exciting discovery, Thomson wanted the people in his laboratory to go full speed ahead testing other chemical elements to see if they also were mixtures of atoms of different weights. At this point World War I broke out, and most of the young scientists had to leave their regular work.

Five years passed before the experiments could be taken up again. Then a student of Thomson's built an improved atom sorter and found that many other elements had atoms of more than one weight. American physicists found still more, and now we know that over three-quarters of all the elements are mixtures of from two to ten different kinds of atoms. The various kinds of atoms of any single element are called *isotopes* of that element. Altogether, more than a thousand isotopes are now known.

With the discovery of isotopes, things began to look complicated once more. True, chemists still had only about 90 kinds of atoms to worry about, but physicists had to deal with more than ten times this many. And the isotopes had to be fitted into the atom map that was already worked out. Knowing the kind and weight of any atom, it is possible to figure out how it is made up. Because all atoms of a single element are chemically alike, we know that all isotopes of this element must have the same number of outer *electrons*. But the difference in weight means that the *nuclei* are different. We can keep the same number of electrons (and protons) and still have a heavier atom just by adding one or more *neutrons* to the nucleus.

Imagine that the atoms of the elements are like apples. There are many types of apples—Delicious, Winesap, Mackintosh, and so on. All Delicious apples look very much alike, but if you cut them open you find that some have more seeds than others. So it is with elements. All atoms of a single element have the same outer shell of electrons, but each isotope has a different number of particles in its nucleus.

Here is the way it works out for the two isotopes of neon. An atom of this element always has a shell of 10 electrons. That is what makes it neon rather than some other element. Ten outer electrons means there must

Each isotope of an element has different particles in its nucleus.

be 10 protons in the nucleus to balance the charge. The 10 protons weigh 10 units, so there must also be 10 neutrons to make up the weight of the "neon 20" nucleus. But to equal the weight of the "neon 22" nucleus, 12 neutrons must be added.

Even hydrogen, the simplest atom, comes in three different forms—there are three isotopes. An ordinary hydrogen atom has just a single proton as a nucleus, with one electron circulating around outside. Scientists suspected there was another isotope, about twice as heavy. They could find no trace of it even with very sensitive atom sorters, so they believed it to be very scarce. How could they increase the amount enough to make it show up?

A group of American scientists hit upon an idea. Under ordinary conditions, hydrogen is a gas, but it can be changed to a liquid by cooling it to about 423 degrees below zero. The experimenters made a gallon of this chilly liquid. Then they allowed it to evaporate. If there were heavier hydrogen atoms in addition to the ordinary kind, more of them would be left behind as the liquid evaporated.

When only a tiny bit of the liquid was left, it was put into an atom sorter. Surely enough, besides ordinary hydrogen atoms, a few heavy hydrogen atoms were found. The picture gives an idea of the make-up of this

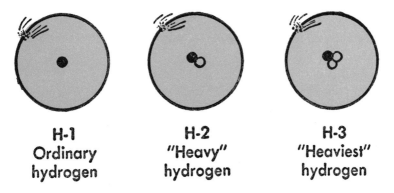

H-1
Ordinary
hydrogen

H-2
"Heavy"
hydrogen

H-3
"Heaviest"
hydrogen

isotope. You see that it is like ordinary hydrogen, except that the nucleus contains a neutron in addition to the proton. Only one hydrogen atom in every 14,000 is a heavy one.

Not many years ago, a triple-weight hydrogen isotope was discovered. There are only about two pounds of this isotope on earth. Besides, it is not permanent like the others but is radioactive, with a half-life of about 12 years.

Have you ever heard of "heavy water?" Remember that a molecule of water is a combination of two atoms of hydrogen with one of oxygen. In ordinary water there will be a molecule, here and there, that has a pair of double-weight hydrogen atoms rather than the lighter kind. There are ways of bringing together most of these heavy molecules in one place. This is called "heavy water." A gallon of it would weigh almost a pound more than a gallon of the ordinary kind. Heavy water played an interesting part in the development of the atomic bomb.

CHAPTER 9

Chipping Away at the Atom

The weather was gloomy that day, and Rutherford sat hunched in a chair in front of his laboratory desk, deep in thought. The year was 1917, and most of his bright young men were away at war. The great physicist was thinking about the experiments of the past years, recalling how busy and productive the laboratory had been, and how much he and his fellow workers had been able to find out about atoms.

However, one thing troubled him greatly. In spite of all that was known, no one had yet found a way of changing one kind of atom into another. Yet for ages this had been happening in the form of radioactivity. Atoms like that of radium went through change after change, and Rutherford himself had been among the first to trace what went on.

All About the Atom

Now he was becoming impatient. "If Nature can make the nucleus of an atom change, why can't we do this in the laboratory?" he wondered. He knew, of course, that long before the days of modern science a group of men who called themselves *alchemists* believed they could find a way of changing iron to gold. Although the work went on for hundreds of years, nobody ever succeeded in making the tiniest speck of gold. But our understanding of things had come a long way since then. Science knew about molecules and atoms, and even about their parts. Certainly the chances of success in changing the atom were now much better than they had ever been.

Rutherford hoisted his lanky body out of the chair and strode over to a cabinet in one corner of the laboratory. "Perhaps the best way to try to change the nucleus of an atom would be to shoot at it with Nature's own high-energy bullets," he said, half to himself. "Here is a speck of Radium-C, which shoots out alpha particles, and now—let me see—yes! Here's that flash counter. Now if I put the Radium-C in a glass tube. . . ."

It would be nice to think that everything went ahead without difficulty from this point on, but such things happen only in stories. Actually, there were many disappointments, and months passed before Ernest Rutherford found what he was looking for. But when he did, he knew that he had done something no man had ever accomplished before. *He had split an atomic nucleus.*

In the experiment, he put the radioactive material in a glass tube. He placed the flash counter outside the tube, where no alphas could reach it. Then he put one gas after another in the tube with the Radium-C. Nothing happened—until he used nitrogen. Then, suddenly, the counter began to flash even when it was as much as a foot away. This meant that some particles were being shot out that could go five or six times as far as the alphas. Rutherford found the particles to be protons.

What happened was that an alpha particle hit a nitrogen nucleus, but instead of bouncing off, *stuck* in

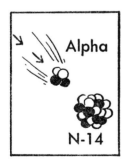  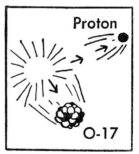

| An alpha heads for an N-14 nucleus . . . | . . and the two combine, only to . . . . | . . break up into a fast proton and an O-17 nucleus. |

it. The commotion caused in the nucleus was then enough to throw a proton out. What remained was the nucleus of an isotope of *oxygen*, O-17. It was like a baseball game in which a playful outfielder catches a fly, slips the baseball into his pocket and throws a tennis ball back to the pitcher instead.

After everything is over, the new nucleus picks up and surrounds itself with enough electrons (there are always some around) to make a complete O-17 atom.

Other experimenters followed up Rutherford's discovery, using a *cloud chamber*. This instrument makes it possible to see the path of the incoming alpha, of the fast proton that is shot out, and even the one made by the new nucleus as it bounces back from the blow. You know how high-flying planes sometimes leave vapor trails behind them in the sky. These streaks are caused by moisture that condenses as the plane passes. In the same way, fast atomic particles can be made to leave trails in the moist air of a cloud chamber to mark their paths. From the appearance of these trails, physicists can usually tell what kind of particles caused them and how fast the particles were going.

The picture shows what is seen in a cloud chamber when an alpha is lucky enough to hit a nitrogen nucleus

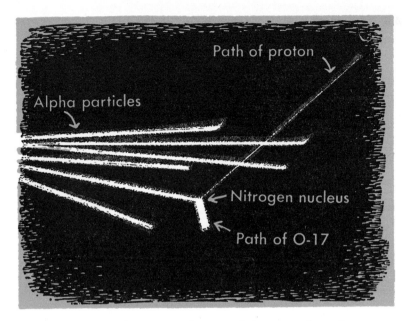

**This is what happens when an alpha particle strikes
a nitrogen nucleus.**

—about once every 300,000 times. The streaks coming
from the left were made by alphas. One of these particles happened to strike a nitrogen nucleus and a proton
was tossed out, making the long, thin streak going
upward to the right. The new O-17 nucleus bounced
off, making the thick, stubby track.

Having found that a nucleus could be changed by
letting natural alpha particles strike it, the scientists next
tried to make their own nuclear bullets to order. They
were impatient with the small number of hits the alphas
were able to make, and they wanted to hurry things
along. Two scientists in Rutherford's laboratory built

an electrical machine that took hydrogen nuclei (protons) and whipped them down a huge pipe until their speed was more than 3,000 miles a second. When the protons were allowed to hit samples of certain elements, nuclear changes took place. Here, less than twenty-five years ago, the science of "atom smashing" began.

Things moved swiftly. In other laboratories, physicists found new and clever ways of giving still more energy to atomic particles, making them serve as nuclear bullets. Suppose you want to make a stone go much faster than it would if you just threw it from your hand. You could tie a string to it, whirl it in a circle overhead until it reached high speed and then let it go.

Using this idea, scientists at the University of California invented a machine called the *cyclotron*. Instead of shooting down a pipe as in the earlier machines, the particles in the cyclotron go round and round in a circle, getting medium-sized electrical boosts each time around. After making a million or so turns, their kinetic energy is so enormous that when they hit a target they cause nuclear changes.

The thing that holds the nuclear particles to their circular path is the bending effect of a huge magnet. In one of the newer cyclotrons, the magnet alone

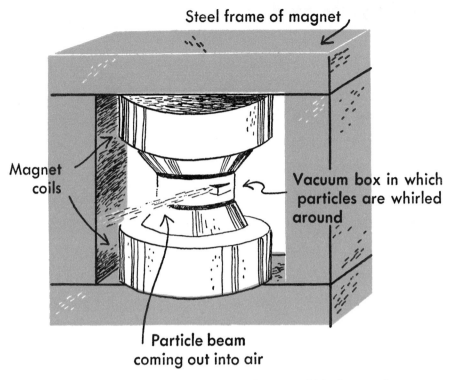

Steel frame of magnet

Magnet coils

Vacuum box in which particles are whirled around

Particle beam coming out into air

In a cyclotron the nuclear particles are whirled around.

weighs 4,000 tons. Using an electrical boost of only a few thousand volts, this machine gives protons as much energy as they would otherwise get from about 350 *million* volts.

Physicists use the word "volt" in rating the energy of the fast particles. They say, "The California cyclotron produces a beam of 350-million-volt protons." Actually, it would take 20,000 such protons to equal the kinetic energy of a flying mosquito. But a proton is about 500 billion billion times lighter than a mosquito!

Particles having millions of volts of energy can do some very important things to the nucleus of an atom.

Within the last few years, still more improvements were made in the design of machines for giving high energy to particles. Since the center part of the magnet is not needed, the newer machines leave it out and have the magnet in the shape of a huge ring instead. One of the biggest of these machines is called the *cosmotron* and is located at the Brookhaven atomic research laboratory near New York City. Its magnet ring is 75 feet across. Around it are concrete walls 10 feet thick to protect the scientists from deadly x-rays that are produced when the particles are whirled around.

In using the cosmotron, some particles are shot in and started on their way. In one second, they go around the ring nearly 4,000,000 times, and travel a total distance greater than from here to the moon. By this time they have an energy of about 2½ *billion* volts! Now they are allowed to strike their target. The operation can be repeated every five seconds.

Not far from the cosmotron, an improved and more powerful atom smasher is being built. Its technical name is quite a mouthful: "alternating gradient synchrotron." The magnet "racetrack" will be an oval 700 feet long—

big enough to hold two football fields. The complete machine will cost about twenty million dollars. It will be able to give protons 25 billion volts of energy. If Rutherford, who built the first machine for this purpose out of packing crates and old tin cans, could only have seen this newest model!

The gigantic machines can do other things besides break up atomic nuclei. If the energy is great enough, entirely new particles called *mesons* are produced. They were first found in *cosmic rays*—the puzzling rays that come to the earth from outer space. The Brookhaven machine was given the name "cosmotron" because it was able to make mesons. Using films and also cloud chambers, physicists are now busy tracking down mesons and finding out more about them.

Not all the big machines are being used for "atom smashing." Some are especially good for speeding up electrons. When these very fast electrons (really beta rays) are allowed to hit a block of metal, powerful and penetrating x-rays are produced. One machine of this kind is called a *betatron*. Its x-rays can go through a yard of steel. Such machines are being used to treat people suffering from tumors or cancer. The rays produced are more powerful than radium.

CHAPTER **10**

What Happens Down Deep?

Day by day, the gigantic machines described in the last chapter are adding to what we know about the nucleus of the atom. Using high-speed particles as bullets, physicists have been able to find out that all nuclei contain protons and neutrons. The only exception is ordinary single-weight hydrogen, which does not have even one neutron in it. The protons and neutrons are clustered together in a space that is not more than a ten-millionth of a millionth of an inch wide, as Rutherford had discovered nearly half a century before.

But scientists wanted to dig deeper into the nucleus. They were curious to know more than its size and what is in it. They wanted to know how it is able to hold together at all! It would seem that the protons in a nucleus ought to push each other apart, because they all have the same kind of electrical charge. This would make it impossible for any nucleus to stay whole. There must be some other kind of force that overcomes the pushing-apart effect. Even now, physicists do not know exactly what this mysterious force may be. The best idea is that the neutrons act like a sort of "glue" that makes the whole cluster of protons hold together.

A good way to think of a nucleus is to imagine it to be like the crater of a volcano, a round hill with a hole in the top. Boys sometimes play a game in which marbles are rolled toward a hole scooped out of the ground. Picture to yourself such a hole with a sloping rim built up all around it. Shoot a fast marble toward

Usually the marble will veer away from the hole.

the hill. Unless it happens to be headed right toward the center, it will roll only part way up the side of the hill and then veer off in another direction, as in the drawing. Seen from some distance away, this would look as if the marble hit the "nucleus" and bounced off, just as the alpha particles did in Rutherford's famous experiments with the gold foil.

Now suppose you shoot another marble, aiming it straight toward the center of the hill. If it has enough energy, it will be able to roll up the sloping side, go over the rim and fall into the crater with a "plop!" This is a model of how an atomic particle can be captured by a nucleus. When the marble falls into the hole, it jiggles all the marbles already there. Once in a while, when the energy of the incoming marble is right, the commotion is enough to throw one or more marbles clear out of the crater. This is exactly what happens when a fast particle enters a nucleus—some other particle may be thrown out.

The crater model can even show how gamma rays are given off in such changes. These rays are caused by the shaking-up of the nuclear particles, just as sound waves were sent out when the incoming marble jiggled all the others.

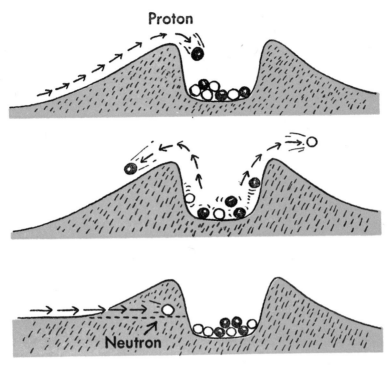

Proton

Neutron

Charged particles go over the top. But a neutron goes
straight through to the crater.

When a *neutron* heads for a nucleus, things are a
little different. Having no electrical charge, a neutron
is not pushed away by the charged nucleus, so it does
not have any hill to climb. You can think of the neutron
as going right *through* the hillside and landing in the
crater without having to climb over. But charged particles usually have to be able to get over the top or they
do not get in at all.

With the crater model of the nucleus to guide them,

experimenters set to work with the huge atom-smashing machines and discovered ways of producing more than a thousand different nuclear changes. Modern science had really made the dream of the ancient alchemists come true. Even atoms of gold could now be made almost to order, but not yet in any quantity. A better way of making new atoms was still to be found.

While this work was going on, other experimenters were making more and more exact measurements of the weights of the different isotopes. The results are among the most accurate measurements ever made, for it is known that they are not wrong by even one part in a million. It is like being able to tell the difference in weight of an automobile when a fly lands on it.

In some of the nuclear experiments, a curious thing was noticed. When the total weight of the fast particle and the target nucleus were added together, the result was not exactly the same as the total weight of all the nuclear pieces left over after the collision. Some weight was either gained or lost during the change. The mystery was soon cleared up, for an explanation of such things had been given by Albert Einstein nearly fifty years earlier, long before the first nuclear change was even dreamed of.

What Happens Down Deep?

Einstein, then a clerk in the Swiss patent office, was only 26 years old. He was just beginning to work out his new ideas about space and time, which became known all over the world as the Theory of Relativity. One of the surprising results of his calculations was that the weight of an object is not always the same, but depends on how fast it is moving. This is certainly very different from the everyday idea that the weight of anything such as a rock is absolutely the same at all times. Einstein figured out that when a thing moved faster, its weight would increase.

At ordinary speeds the change is far too tiny to be measured. For instance, a 20-ton airplane flying at 400 miles an hour is only a few millionths of an ounce heavier than when standing still. But when anything moves at a speed up near the speed of light, which is 186,000 miles a second, the gain in weight becomes much larger. Atomic particles can get up to such speeds, and the gain in weight actually shows up as Einstein figured. An electron, for example, that is hurled down a vacuum tube by 3 million volts, will be going about 99 percent as fast as light and will weigh over six times as much as normal.

The Theory of Relativity says something else that is

even more surprising. It explains where all "atomic energy" comes from. Earlier in this book you saw that an object could have energy given to it, and that you could get such an object to do work for you by making it give up some of its energy. The relativity theory adds something new by saying that *matter can be changed into energy, and energy can be changed into matter.* This means that, under certain conditions, part of the weight of an object can disappear and create some energy in its place. Going the opposite way, energy can be "frozen" into the form of matter. All this is tied together in a mathematical formula that we see

Dr. Albert Einstein developed the famous formula $E = mc^2$.

even in the newspapers these days. It looks like this:

$$E=mc^2$$

It reads: "E equals m c squared." E stands for energy, m for the amount of matter that appears or disappears, and c is the scientific label for the speed of light. This speed is a very big number, and that means that if even the tiniest bit of matter could be made to disappear, an enormous amount of energy would be given off. For instance, we can calculate the amount of this "material energy" in a single drop of water. If we could find a way to set it free, it would be enough to send a four-motored plane around the world five times!

If we could set it free—but can we? The answer at the present time is, "Partly." It happens in every nuclear change.

After the atom sorter had revealed the exact weights of various atoms, scientists were able to check the connection between matter and energy. They took fast particles from the great machines and fed them into a cloud chamber, where they could watch what happened when a particle hit an atomic nucleus. The vapor tracks told them just how fast each particle was going before and after the collision. The kinetic energy of the "bullet" beforehand could then be compared with the kinetic energy of all the pieces afterward.

Sometimes there was a definite gain in energy. This was really "atomic energy," but where did it come from? When they checked up on all the particles after the smash-up, they found there was a slight *loss* in the total weight. This is where the extra energy came from —*matter had been changed into energy*. The amount worked out to be just what the Einstein formula called for.

In some of the experiments there was a slight loss in the total *energy*, but in such cases there was always just the right gain in *weight* to even things out. Dozens of measurements showed that the Einstein idea was correct. He had proved that it was not the weight or the energy that always stayed the same, but the total of *both taken together*.

One thing was still disappointing. With all their big machines, the amount of energy that scientists could get out of the nucleus was so tiny that it seemed it would never be of any practical use. Until just a few years ago, this is where Nature seemed to draw the line. Atomic energy was like a locked-up treasure. We could only wonder at it, but could not use it. Then came some great discoveries that showed how to get at this treasure. This brought us into the Atomic Age.

CHAPTER 11

Nuclear Fission

If the huge machines such as the cyclotron were unable to get much energy out of the nucleus by shooting faster and faster charged particles at it, what was to be done?

The answer was: Try neutrons instead. Having no charge, a neutron could get into a nucleus without climbing the "hill." The surprising thing was that slow neutrons were found to work better than fast ones. Neutrons can be slowed down by letting them go through paraffin, carbon or some other material containing a great many lightweight atoms. The neutrons lose their energy by bumping into the other atoms, just as a fast walker might be slowed down when he strides into a crowd.

At the University of Rome, a young Italian experimenter named Enrico Fermi wanted to see what would happen if slow neutrons hit uranium. At that time, the uranium atom was the heaviest one known. His idea was that by making a neutron stick inside a uranium nucleus, an even heavier atom might be formed.

He tried the experiment, and while the results were very puzzling, they seemed to be worth following up. More experiments of this kind were done in other laboratories. German scientists found that atoms of

Barium appears when neutrons hit uranium atoms.

barium were left after the experiment was over, which only added to the puzzle. Barium is a middle-weight atom, about half as heavy as uranium. What was it doing here? Could it have been formed by the splitting of the uranium nucleus? In all the other nuclear changes ever seen, the weights of the nuclei shifted by only a few numbers. Here was a change in weight of nearly a hundred. If this was really what happened, it meant the biggest nuclear smash so far. Rutherford missed seeing this, for he had died the year before.

It was the beginning of the year 1939. Hitler had come to power, and many German scientists were forced to leave the country. Among these were some who carried the news of uranium splitting to the Institute of Theoretical Physics in Copenhagen, Denmark. Professor Niels Bohr, the head of the institute, was about to leave for the United States to discuss some problems with Einstein. When he told American physicists what his German friends had found, there was great excitement.

Experimenters in New York and California checked the fact that uranium nuclei actually break up the way the German scientists believed. In England and France, too, other scientists got further proof. The break-ups were recorded in the form of bright wiggles on the front of a kind of television tube, as the drawing shows. There was no longer any doubt. Slow neutrons really could split the uranium nucleus.

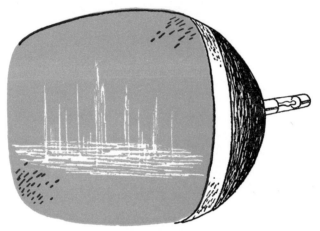

Each streak shows the breakdown of a uranium nucleus.

This kind of splitting into two nearly equal pieces was called *nuclear fission*. Every nuclear change known up to that time was just the chipping off of small pieces of the nucleus—a proton, a neutron, perhaps an alpha. This was different. It was really "atom smashing," with the nucleus chopped just about in half. And the important thing is that the fission of a nucleus gives us *ten to a hundred times as much energy* as other kinds of nuclear actions.

The trouble with the previous nuclear changes was

that they would not keep themselves going. It is very much like trying to build a fire and finding that you get only a harmless shower of sparks which soon go out. If some way could be found to make each spark set fire to more material, the flames would quickly spread and you would have a first-rate blaze that produced much heat (energy).

In the fission action, the big question was: Are more neutrons set free when a uranium nucleus breaks up? If so, these neutrons could cause still more uranium to fission, and so on. This would mean that just a single slow neutron would be needed to start things off. One atom would split. In doing so, it would split others. Fission would go faster and faster, spreading through the whole material and setting great quantities of energy

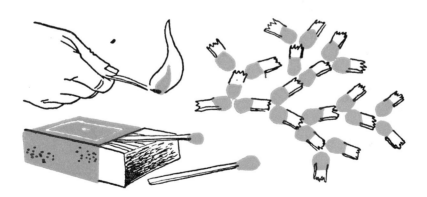

The lighted match starts a "chain reaction."

free. This would be a *chain reaction.*

Several scientists found that neutrons were really produced when a uranium nucleus splits, so at least it seemed that a chain reaction was possible. Bohr found that a heavy nucleus like uranium acts something like a big drop of water on a greasy plate. If the drop is hit by something, it may wobble and tremble so strongly that it pinches in two. When this happens, a few small drops are spattered out. In the same way, a uranium nucleus will split when struck by a neutron, spattering out newly-formed neutrons which strike out to make still other nuclei split, and so on.

To the scientists, things were becoming as interesting as a good detective story. The next step was to find out

The big blob of water on a greasy plate splits when hit by a falling drop.

which of the known isotopes of uranium would give the chain reaction. Natural uranium is a mixture of three isotopes, with weights of 234, 235 and 238. Over 99 percent is the heaviest kind, U-238. Of a one-inch cube of uranium, almost all would be U-238. A piece about as big as a pea would be U-235, and a speck the size of the head of a pin would be U-234. Small amounts of the isotopes were separated in an atom sorter, and it turned out that U-235 can capture slow neutrons and then break down by fission. U-238 can capture fast neutrons, but stays whole when this happens. As for U-234, there is not enough to bother about.

It was clear that the way to get a chain reaction with U-235 was to get most of the U-238 out of the way. The big problem was to find a good way to separate these two uranium isotopes from each other.

What happens to the U-238 when it captures a neutron? Something interesting—and very useful. Instead of breaking apart by fission, the new atom throws out a beta particle and becomes *neptunium*, the next heavier element after uranium, and never known before. So after all, what Fermi hoped to find in his first experiments did come about.

Neptunium itself is radioactive. It throws out another

electron and becomes the next element, called *pluto-nium*. And a plutonium nucleus can break up by fission —like U-235—when a neutron hits it, giving off enormous quantities of energy.

This much was known by the autumn of 1939, when Hitler's armies invaded Poland. The war was on in Europe and the scientists of different countries could no longer compare their work. Some of the German and French physicists were able to get to England, where they began to discuss the chances of using nuclear fission in a bomb. They figured out that if all the atoms in a single pound of U-235 could suddenly be split by fission, the blast would be as powerful as 20 *million* pounds of TNT—one of the strongest chemical explosives known.

Before long, the British government set up a research group to work out the possibilities of making a bomb. The director was J. J. Thomson's son, George Thomson. The first problem was how to separate U-235 from U-238 in large amounts, because these were isotopes of the same element. There was no simple chemical way to do this, so other ways were suggested. One was the use of an atom sorter. The magnet would swing the lighter isotope around a little more sharply

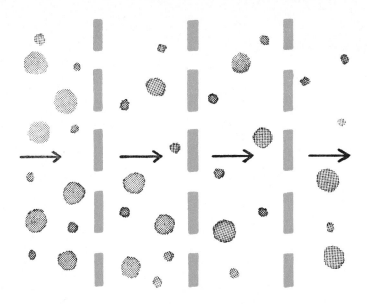

This is what happens when two kinds of gas stream through a set of fine filters.

than the heavier, and so the two could be separated. But a fantastic number of machines of this kind would be needed to work on the big quantities of uranium required.

Another way would be to make the uranium combine with some other element to form a gas. Then this gas could be allowed to stream through very fine filters. The molecules containing U-235 are lighter than the ones containing U-238, so more of them would get through each filter. If the process were repeated thousands of times, the separation would become more and more perfect. Still other ways were discussed, too.

Meanwhile, in the United States, Einstein and other

scientists urged President Roosevelt to start research in this country. Then, early in December of 1941, came the attack on Pearl Harbor, and we were at war. The government gave money to several universities to begin work on atomic energy.

In 1942, Enrico Fermi and his group of scientists at the University of Chicago built what they called an atomic *pile* to see if they could start a chain reaction that would keep itself going. They laid out bricks of very pure graphite, which is the form of carbon used in lead pencils. Between the graphite bricks they put small lumps of uranium metal. This was built up, layer on layer, in the shape of a flattened ball nearly three times as tall as a man. The purpose of the graphite blocks was to act as a *moderator*, slowing down the newly-formed neutrons so they can enter other U-235 nuclei and keep the chain reaction going.

In order to control the reaction and prevent its going too fast, strips of cadmium metal were placed in special slots through the pile. Cadmium soaks up neutrons, so the strips act as a brake to slow the reaction down. If the experimenters want the action to speed up, the strips can be pulled part way out of the pile. If the action goes too fast, they can be shoved back in.

The number of neutrons is measured at all times by a *Geiger counter*, named after Rutherford's assistant, Hans Geiger, who invented it. This is a gas-filled tube which can be made to flash a light or sound a loud click whenever a fast particle or a gamma ray shoots through.

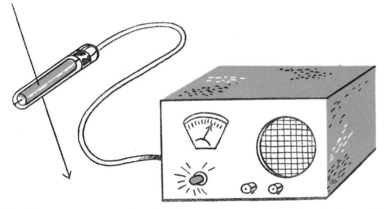

The Geiger counter signals when a fast particle shoots through.

December 2, 1942, was a turning point in the history of nuclear physics. On that day, Fermi and his helpers set the pile going.

Every person in that secret laboratory watched tensely as Fermi ordered the control strips pulled out, a little at a time. The meters began clicking, faster and faster. The pile was working! Quickly, the strips were pushed back in. To everybody's relief, the counters slowed down again. For the first time in history, scientists had started a nuclear chain reaction that could keep itself going.

Now things really began to hum. Our government ordered the building of huge plants for making nuclear materials for atomic bombs. Whole cities were constructed almost overnight. At Hanford, Washington, three gigantic piles, each as tall as a five-story building, were constructed. By this time, the scientists were calling them *nuclear reactors*. The main purpose of this plant was to let fast neutrons strike atoms of U-238 and so manufacture plutonium. In this way, the greater part of the uranium, which up to now was useless for fission, was made available for this purpose.

The fission taking place in a reactor develops heat, which must be gotten rid of. The Chicago reactor was never allowed to produce more heat than would make a teakettle of water boil in about two minutes. Compare this with the Hanford reactors, which needed the waters of the mighty Columbia River to cool them. These huge amounts of energy need not be thrown away, but can be put to good use, as you will soon see.

At Oak Ridge, Tennessee, a plant covering hundreds of acres of ground was built to separate U-235 by the filter method. By the summer of 1944 production was

The Oak Ridge plant covers hundreds of acres of ground.

going full speed. A few months later, a factory for separating U-235 from U-238 by the atom-sorter method was also in operation at Oak Ridge.

We now had ways of producing large amounts of the two materials that would be suitable for a bomb—U-235 and plutonium. How could such a bomb be set off?

Suppose that a single slow neutron is wandering around in a big piece of U-235 or plutonium. (There are some neutrons around all the time, probably knocked out of atoms by cosmic rays.) This single neutron lodges in a nucleus, breaking it apart by fission. When this happens, *more than one* additional neutron is set free. Suppose that it is two, on the average. If both these two neutrons cause fission in two more nuclei, we then get *four* the next time. These four produce *eight* the following time, and so on. The number builds up very rapidly.

Perhaps you have heard the story of the ancient king who wanted to reward one of his subjects for saving his life. "Name any treasure you wish," said the king.

"It is known," the man answered, "that your majesty is fond of playing chess. As my reward, I would like one grain of wheat for the first square on the chessboard, two grains for the second square, four for the next,—each time, twice as many grains, until all 64 squares are used."

The king laughed. "These few grains of wheat are no deserving reward for you," he said, "when you might ask for all the gold and jewels in the kingdom. I beg you to change your mind." But the man insisted, and so the king ordered the grain counted out.

Before long, the royal chamberlain came running excitedly to the king. "Sire," he cried, "there is not enough wheat in the entire kingdom to pay this man!"

Like most of us, the king did not realize how fast a number mounts up by doubling again and again. His gift would have required over 18 billion billion grains, or enough to fill a cube about 4 miles on each edge!

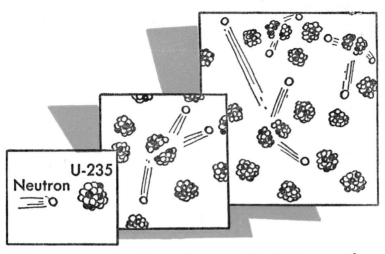

**When a neutron breaks a nucleus apart by fission, countless
other fissions follow.**

So it is with the repeated doubling of the number of
neutrons. Here, one doubling follows another in less
than a millionth of a second. This means that, almost
instantly, a gigantic number of fissions takes place, each
one setting energy free. The result is an explosion of
unbelievable power. This is the A-bomb.

One more thing needs clearing up: If stray neutrons
are always around, why is it that every piece of U-235
or plutonium does not explode as soon as it is prepared?
The answer is that in a fairly small lump, the chain is
broken by neutrons escaping to the outside before they
can find nuclei to blast apart, so the action never really
gets started. But in a piece about as big as a baseball, the
chain reaction will go ahead because more neutrons will

form than escape. In the A-bomb, the fission material is kept as two separate pieces, each too small to blow up by itself. When the bomb is to be exploded, the two chunks are rammed together. The resulting big piece goes off in less than a thousandth of a second.

From here on, the story is well known. An A-bomb was built and successfully tested on the New Mexico desert on July 16, 1945. On August 6th, an American bomber dropped a U-235 bomb on the Japanese city of Hiroshima. Three days later, a plutonium bomb was dropped on Nagasaki. Both cities were practically destroyed. Then, for the first time, the world knew something about what had been going on in secret since the beginning of the war six years before. Within a month, the Japanese surrendered, and the war in the Pacific was over.

CHAPTER 12

Big Atoms from Little Ones

What keeps the sun shining? This question, which had troubled scientists for centuries, has now been answered in a surprising way. The atomic nucleus furnishes the enormous energy that the sun and the other stars have been pouring out into space for billions of years.

Our sun, on which all life on earth depends, is a typical star—a huge, glowing ball of white-hot gases. Astronomers know of other stars that are thousands of times brighter than the sun, and there are many that are much weaker. The sun, our middle-sized star, is producing light and heat at the rate of nearly a *million billion billion* horsepower. The tiny earth, 93,000,000 miles away, scoops up only about half a billionth of this. Even so, the amount is tremendous. The energy we get from the sun in three minutes would be enough to run all the world's machinery for an entire year.

At first, people wondered if the sun got its energy by burning something, but this idea had to be given up. If the entire sun were made of coal, it would last only a few thousand years. But science knows that the earth is several billion years old, so the sun must have been shining for at least that length of time. Another idea was that heat and light are produced as the materials of the sun gradually fall in toward the center. Here again, figures showed that even this would not keep the sun going for a long enough time.

When radioactivity was discovered, scientists saw that this might be the one thing that could supply enough energy to explain the working of the sun and stars. In radioactivity, you remember, fast particles and gamma rays may be given off as the nuclei break down. In a piece of any radioactive material, the energy of these particles and waves is changed into heat. For this reason, a lump of radium is always slightly warmer than the things around it. This does not amount to much, and if all the heat given off by an ounce of radium could be caught, it would take over eight hours to get enough to boil a cup of water! However, if very large amounts of radioactive material could be gotten together, the total heat would be very great. But as far as we know, the sun does not have much natural radio-active material in it. The sun and the stars are mostly hydrogen.

Deep inside the sun, conditions are far different from anything we can imagine. The temperature at the center is nearly 40,000,000 degrees, and the layers above are pushing downward more than a million times harder than the water at the bottom of our oceans. We can only try to guess what such conditions are like. Probably the electrons of the atoms have become stripped away from their nuclei. Then, without the protection of the outer electrons, it should be fairly easy for the speeding nuclei to react when they hit each other.

This idea for explaining the energy of the sun and stars was suggested by physicists just before World War II. The action that seems most likely is that four hydrogen atoms combine to form a single atom of helium. This combination of light atoms to form heavier ones is called *nuclear fusion*. This reaction had not yet been done on earth, simply because experimenters had no way of getting the high temperatures necessary to start it. Still, it was possible to figure out on paper how much energy would be produced. The key was Ein-

High temperature causes four hydrogen atoms to fuse and form
a helium atom plus energy.

stein's famous formula $E=mc^2$. From their atom-sorter
experiments, physicists know exactly how much four
atoms of hydrogen weigh. One atom of helium weighs
just a little *less* than this total, so the weight left over
could be set free in the form of energy. For every
pound of hydrogen used, about ⅛ ounce of matter
would disappear. In its place would appear as much
energy as we get by burning 12,000 tons of coal.

Here at last was a supply of energy big enough to
explain what happens in the stars. The details were
worked out. It turned out that in the sun, other nuclei
such as carbon, oxygen and nitrogen also take part in
the reaction, but they are left without change after
everything is over. The only material actually used up is

hydrogen, and there is enough in the sun and in the stars to keep them going for billions of years more.

After scientists learned that great quantities of energy could be set free by putting together hydrogen atoms to form helium, they began to wonder if they could actually do this on earth. There were good reasons for believing it would be possible. Think of the chemical elements as boulders resting on the slopes of a valley. The lighter boulders are arranged along the steeper side of the valley, while the heavier ones are on the more gentle slope. Near the bottom of the valley, where the ground is almost level, are the boulders of in-between weight. If there should be a slight earthquake, some of the boulders on the slopes will be jarred loose and come tumbling down into the valley, but the ones that are already near the bottom will

During an earthquake, boulders on the ground would hardly move.

not move much.

So it is with the elements. The heaviest ones can break down by fission into lighter elements, giving up large amounts of energy, as you saw in the last chapter. But the lightest elements, by *fusion* into heavier elements, can give up much greater energy. The elements in between give very much less energy when they change.

By the time World War II had ended, physicists were again thinking of ways of producing nuclear fusion. They had already found the secret of fission, and here was the possibility of getting hundreds of times as much energy. Besides, the materials needed, such as hydrogen, are plentiful, while uranium is very scarce. The trouble was that the lightweight nuclei would have to be smashed together with great force in order to get them to combine. The only thing that could make the nuclei move fast enough would be high temperature. But by this time there *was* a way of getting very high temperatures—the fission bomb. Why not use a fission bomb as a "match" to "light up" the hydrogen?

When the scientists figured out the possibilities, it seemed that neither the ordinary single-weight hydrogen isotope nor even the double-weight one would work with the fission bombs they had at that time. But the scarce triple-weight H-3 seemed to have a better chance. The government built a huge reactor plant on the Savannah River in South Carolina for the purpose of making H-3. The cost of this factory was one and a half billion dollars, and the H-3 coming from it will probably cost about a million dollars a pound!

From this point on, we can only guess at what is done, since the entire project is kept secret by the government. We do know that on the morning of November 1, 1952, a small island in the Eniwetok group was practically destroyed by the testing of our first H-bomb. The explosion was estimated to have the power of five million tons of TNT—hundreds of times more than an A-bomb. Probably only a small amount of H-3, mixed with H-2, was used. A uranium fission bomb at the center could set off the mixture of H-2 and H-3, and then this "fuse" would be able to set off the main charge. The best guess is that the main charge was a chemical compound of lithium, the next heavier element after helium. The nuclear particles of the Li-6 atom and the H-2 atom rearrange themselves to form two helium nuclei having a tremendous amount of energy.

Further tests have been carried out by our government since that time, and are continuing at present.

CHAPTER 13

More Power for More People

The last two chapters told about the tremendous energy that can be released by nuclear fission or fusion. If the energy is set free all at once, it amounts to nothing more than a bomb, but if the rate of release is controlled and spread over a period of time, the energy can be put to practical use. Ever since the discovery of fission, scientists and engineers have wondered about the possibility of building nuclear power plants for running the machines of industry, for transportation, and for lighting and heating our homes.

There are good reasons for wanting to build nuclear power plants. First of all, they could deliver hundreds or thousands of times as much energy as we get from present power plants that burn ordinary chemical fuels such as coal, oil or gas. Then, too, nuclear materials could be much more easily shipped from one place to another than chemical fuels. A single pound of U-235 can give as much energy as the burning of 1,300 tons of coal. However, the biggest reason for looking to the atom for power is that the world's supply of coal, oil and gas may not last more than a few hundred years. By the time your grandchildren grow up, they may actually be faced with this problem.

Luckily, a start has already been made toward solving at least part of the problem. The nuclear reactor is the answer. If we could use the heat produced in a reactor to operate steam engines or steam turbines, we would be able to conserve much of our natural fuels.

The reactor takes the place of a furnace. Except for this, a nuclear power station is just like the kind we now have. The engines turn electric generators and the power is sent out over electric lines to places where it is used. The only difference is that the original heat is supplied by nuclear changes instead of by the burning of coal.

One of the biggest problems is protection of the people working around the reactor from dangerous radiations. This means that a reactor must be surrounded by a heavy wall of concrete or lead. This makes the setup very heavy and clumsy, so there is not much chance of its being used to run an automobile or air-plane, or for heating your home. However, the heavy shield is less of a drawback in building a nuclear power station, or an engine for a submarine or large ship.

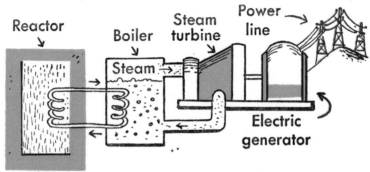

The reactor furnishes heat to run the power plant.

The general arrangement might be something like the one in the picture. The water that is boiled to produce steam must not be allowed to come in contact with the reactor itself because of the danger of carrying harmful radiations out with it. A separate liquid must be used to carry heat from the reactor and give it to the boiler.

Propelling a submarine is one very good use for a nuclear plant. Such a vessel can cruise under water for almost unlimited distances without having to come to the surface. A working engine for this purpose was built and tested at a secret location in the mountains of Idaho, hundreds of miles from the nearest ocean. It was run on a make-believe underwater crossing of the Atlantic Ocean in the summer of 1954. Then a power plant of the same kind was installed in an actual submarine, the *Nautilus*, which was designed for this purpose. The *Nautilus* made its first successful trial runs early in 1955. A second nuclear-powered submarine, the *Seawolf*, was already under construction at that time.

It is true that a nuclear power station uses very little uranium or other nuclear fuel, but would we have enough if we started to build such plants all over the country, or all over the world? At present, there are only a few places where uranium is mined in large quantities. Of course, other rich deposits may still be found. That is why our government offers a large money prize to anyone who discovers new uranium rock deposits. Prospectors carrying portable Geiger counters are searching at many places all over the country, hoping to make a "strike."

In the meantime, a new scientific discovery may actually make it possible to manufacture new nuclear materials in large enough amounts for our uses. At the Atomic Energy Commission plant in Idaho, a reactor that produces power and at the same time makes nuclear fuel for use in other reactors has been working since 1951. This may sound as impossible as a coal furnace that makes new coal while it operates, yet it is true. The reactor is called a *breeder*, because the active material reproduces itself, just as cattle breed more cattle.

In one form of breeder reactor, a little U-235 is mixed with thorium, which is a much more plentiful element than uranium. The fission of U-235 produces slow neutrons. When one of these enters a thorium nucleus, two beta particles are shot out, one after the other. The remaining nucleus is a new isotope of uranium, U-233. The useful thing about U-233 is that it can be split by fission, just like U-235 and plutonium. The U-233 can be removed from the breeder and used in a separate reactor. In this way, the breeder reactor continually makes new nuclear fuel.

The Atomic Energy Commission says that, counting only the uranium and thorium already discovered, we should then be able to supply the world's energy needs for nearly 2,000 years! It is possible, too, that ways will be found to use fusion reactions for power. This would give us almost endless amounts of nuclear fuel.

There is one question left to be answered. Can nuclear

power be produced cheaply enough so that it will take the place of power from coal? If the breeder idea is a success, then there certainly will be no shortage of nuclear materials, and the cost of this fuel will be low. But there are other problems to think about. Nuclear power plants will be expensive to build and to run, and the dangerous materials will have to be handled without harming workers or the people living near by.

Nuclear energy will be brought to less advanced countries.

In spite of the difficulties, several nuclear power plants should be in operation within a few years. One of the largest is being built near Pittsburgh. It will cost 85 million dollars and will supply enough power for a city of 100,000 people. A power reactor being built in the northwest part of England may be ready even before this. Several other European countries, as well as Canada, are planning to build such reactors in the near future.

In most of these countries, and especially in the United States, power is already plentiful and fairly cheap. But think of the advantages of bringing nuclear energy to some of the less advanced countries. The main reason for the slow development of many of these lands is the shortage of power. Most of their work must still be done by animals or by human labor. The United States and other countries could lend nuclear materials and engineering help to the undeveloped regions of Asia and Africa. This would make the neglected parts of the world flourish. In just a few years, they could make more progress than in many centuries before.

CHAPTER 14

Atoms at Work

Suppose you are standing inside a huge building, look-ing up at a cube of green-painted concrete as tall as a three-story house. On a platform above, workers are ramming a long metal rod into one of the hundreds of holes that stud the side of the cube. Piping and electrical cables mark out a queer pattern crisscrossing the green wall. Off to one side, switches click and signal lamps flash. The whining sound of an electric motor is heard.

Scientists in laboratory coats stand by, watching in-strument dials, occasionally turning switches or stopping to make notes. Deep inside the cube, behind protective walls seven feet thick, trillions of uranium atoms are splitting apart, giving out energy steadily but silently.

This is the Atomic Energy Commission's reactor at Oak Ridge, Tennessee. It is not being used to drive engines or heat buildings. Instead, it is doing something never before possible—it is creating new and useful isotopes of the chemical elements.

Following the invention of the cyclotron about twenty-five years earlier, physicists used these machines to shoot fast particles at atoms of various elements. In many cases, nuclear changes took place, as you already know. Once the machine was stopped, the newly-formed material usually stayed just as it was. But in some cases, the new substances, after removal from the cyclotron, kept on breaking down over a period of time, just like radioactive elements. They were not radium or thorium or any of the radioactive materials found in the earth. They were new isotopes of ordinary elements. For instance, when common salt (sodium chloride, NaCl) is hit by fast nuclei of heavy hydrogen, some of the ordinary sodium atoms, Na-23, are changed to Na-24. This isotope is not found at all in natural salt. It is radioactive, and breaks down by shooting out beta and gamma rays, with a half-life of about 15 hours. Na-24 is called radio-sodium.

Man-made radioactive isotopes of this kind are called *radio-isotopes*. Nearly a thousand different radio-isotopes, belonging to almost every known chemical ele-

The man handling radioactive materials wears a protective suit.

ment, have been made. We now have radio-iron, radio-cobalt, radio-gold and many others.

Now, with reactors in operation, scientists have a way of manufacturing radio-isotopes in much larger amounts than ever before. A piece of the material to be activated is put into a small aluminum container which is shoved into the reactor through one of the many holes in the concrete shield. Here the substance is allowed to "cook" for a few days, or for several months, as neutrons swarm through it. After enough of the atoms have been made active, the material is taken out and stored in a special room having thick, protective walls.

The "hot" materials must be handled with great care, so that the workers are not harmed by dangerous neutrons and other radiations that are given off. Of course, "handled" is not the right word, for it would be fatal to touch some of these radio-isotopes directly. They have to be picked up and moved about and put through entire chemical processes without ever coming within yards of a human worker.

The room where radio-isotopes are kept is like a weird kind of super market. Instead of going around with a cart and selecting the things they want, the attendants work from behind a barricade in an adjoining room. They use strange robot-like machines with jointed metal arms and fingers to pick out the materials they need. Watching through a tank of protective liquid, or in a tilted mirror, or even with a special TV hook-up, they guide the mechanical hands that do the work in the "hot" room.

Everything in this room is done mechanically from outside. The attendant pulls a handle. He watches as a drawer in a concrete storage box slowly rolls open. Instantly a warning bell begins to ring. A Geiger counter, set off by the rays, makes the ringing continue as long as the drawer stays open. The operator moves other control knobs. The steel hands of his mechanical "slave" lift a bottle of active material from the drawer, take off the cap, draw out a little of the liquid through a tube and squirt it into a smaller bottle. This bottle will then

The operator uses mechanical "hands" to move active material.

be put into a thick box made of lead and shipped to the place where it is to be used. If the isotope has a short half-life, it is rushed to the user by airplane.

From the time the Oak Ridge atomic super market opened in 1946, nearly 40,000 shipments have been made. Yet radio-isotopes are so powerful that the active atoms in this entire output weigh less than one ounce! A single year's production from Oak Ridge has more activity than all the refined radium in the world, and costs less than a thousandth as much.

What happens to radio-isotopes after they are delivered to the buyer? This depends on the kind of work to be done. The main uses are in treating disease and in scientific research. Isotopes that give off strong rays are used by doctors to destroy diseased cells in the body. Weaker and less destructive isotopes are used in research work as *tracers*. They leave a trail that scientists can follow with sensitive instruments. Engineers, too, have put radio-isotopes to work, as you will see.

To find out how doctors use tracers, let us see what happens when a patient has a brain tumor—a growth that is in danger of pressing on the brain. The doctor injects a small amount of radio-phosphorus into the patient's body. The phosphorus is carried by the blood

Doctors use the radiation detector to locate diseased cells.

stream to all parts of the body, but for some reason most of it is taken up by the tumor if there is one. By moving a radiation detector back and forth over the skull, the doctor can tell whether a tumor is present, and can find its position so that it can be removed by a surgical operation.

Radio-iodine, made in an atomic reactor, can help physicians treat diseases of the thyroid gland. This gland is located in the throat and is very important to health. The patient is given a drink containing a little radio-iodine. Most of this active isotope is taken up by the thyroid. The amount it holds on to is measured from outside by a radiation detector, and this tells the doctor about the condition of the gland.

In the actual treatment to destroy growths such as tumors or cancers in the body, x-rays and the gamma rays from radium have been used for a long time. These rays can be used if the growth is not too deep. Otherwise, the skin and outer parts of the body will be harmed before enough radiation gets down deep enough to do its work. Recently, two small disks of cesium metal, prepared in a nuclear reactor, were used to build one of the world's most powerful treatment units. The cost was only a few thousand dollars, but the machine gives as much radiation as 20 million dollars' worth of radium.

In the past, when doctors wanted to treat a growth located deep inside the body, they would insert in it a tiny "seed" of radioactive material which did its work by sending out rays within the growth itself. After a time, this seed had to be removed to avoid too much radiation. Now, with radio-isotopes on hand, the doctor can choose one that need not be removed once it has done its work. One of these is radio-gold, which has a half-life of only three days. Little pellets of this isotope are inserted into the tumor. They are actually shot in from a special "gun." By the time the treatment is complete, the activity of the gold has dropped to practically nothing. The pellets can be left in place permanently without harm to the patient.

There are many other ways in which radio-isotopes are being used in treating disease, and new methods are being worked out all the time. The greater use of radio-isotopes by physicians all over the world will relieve much human suffering and will mean longer and more useful lives for many people. Medical research scientists call radio-isotopes the most important medical discovery since the invention of the microscope.

In the body, radio-isotopes act exactly the same way as ordinary isotopes of the same element. This makes it possible to tell just what happens to each substance that is taken in. For example, if salt containing some radio-sodium atoms is fed to a person, scientists can trace where it goes and how long it stays in the body. In this way, they have discovered that every part of the body is constantly being made over as new materials from food replace the ones already there. The surprising fact is that the human body is almost completely rebuilt every year. Even the bones are replaced this way. One exception is the iron, mainly in the red blood cells, which stays around much longer.

Radio-isotopes help farmers and cattle-growers, too. At Brookhaven laboratories, not far from the gigantic cosmotron, agricultural scientists buried a slug of radio-cobalt in the ground and planted corn in wider and wider rings around it. They found that entirely new varieties of corn were created by the effects of the gamma rays. From such experiments, experts look forward to finding ways of growing better food crops.

One of Nature's greatest puzzles is the way in which green plants use the sun's energy to build up chemical materials out of water and carbon dioxide. By using radio-carbon, research workers have come one step nearer understanding how this happens. Plants were allowed to "breathe" carbon dioxide whose molecules were built with this active isotope. After only one minute, the active atoms appeared in more than fifty separate compounds composing the plant.

When tomato plants were fed small amounts of radio-zinc, it collected inside the seeds. A slice of the fruit was laid on a photographic film, taking its own picture by rays from the active zinc atoms in it. Experiments such

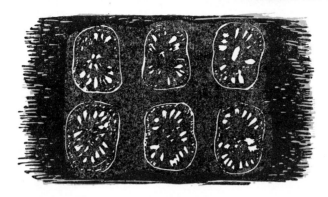

Slices of radioactive tomatoes take their own picture.

as these will probably show how to increase crop production and so prevent famine in many parts of the world where food is scarce.

Many crop failures are due to damage by insects. Radio-isotopes can help here too. Scientists at an English government laboratory dabbed insects with radioactive paint and let them loose on a field of turnip plants. Geiger counters showed how the destructive bugs wandered from one plant to another, pointing out the first step in controlling them. Other scientists are experimenting with mosquitoes that have been made radioactive. The results show how long these disease-carrying insects live, how far they can fly and what they feed on.

Even after food is produced on the farm of cattle ranch, there is still the possibility of loss through spoiling. By giving potatoes a short exposure to rays from a reactor, they can be kept as long as two years without rotting or sprouting and in no way endangering their use as food. The treatment costs less than one-fifth of a cent per pound. And at the University of Michigan, research shows that pork can be sterilized and made safe by exposing it to the rays from radio-cesium.

Engineers were among the first to put tracers to work. One of the most interesting uses is for measuring and controlling the thickness of sheet metal, paper or plastic as it is formed by rollers. In a steel mill, a small "pill" of radio-strontium is mounted under the moving metal sheet. The strength of the beta rays picked up by a detector on the other side of the strip depends on how

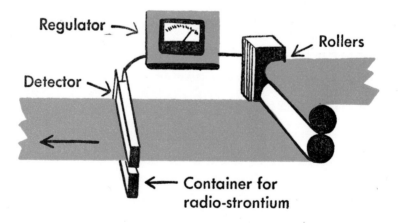

Active atoms automatically control the thickness of the sheet.

thick the metal is. If the thickness changes, the detector automatically sends a signal to a motor and it corrects the spacing of the rollers. Without stopping the machine, the thickness of the sheet is kept from changing even as much as half a thousandth of an inch. Several hundred of these "atomic watchmen" are already in use in factories.

Radio-isotopes help the oil industry in many ways. One thing they can do is to act as messengers in the long pipe lines that carry oil, gasoline or kerosene between places hundreds of miles apart. These pipes must carry different kinds of oil at different times, one after another. How can the workers know when one grade of oil has all come through and another has started? Simply by squirting in a little radioactive oil when they send a new batch into the pipe. When the active atoms reach the far end of the line they set off a detector. An attendant then turns a valve that sends the new kind of oil into a separate tank. This single trick is now saving oil companies almost a million dollars a year.

If small amounts of radio-isotopes are put into automobile tires or machine parts or even floor wax, engineers can detect the tiny amounts of material that rub off after only a short time of use. In this way, automotive engineers were able to prove that car engines wear out about three times as fast in city driving as in high-speed driving on the open road.

Chemists report that the rays from active isotopes can help them make new plastics, insect poisons and other chemical products. At the University of Michigan, a gas called ethylene was showered with gamma rays from radio-cobalt. It changed into polyethylene, the plastic used to make flexible bottles for drugs and lotions. One of the big oil companies is setting up a special laboratory to study new products that can be made by radiation. The rays will come from a piece of radio-cobalt that has been "cooking" in the Brookhaven reactor for about two and a half years.

Even in the field of art, nuclear energy seems to be finding things to do. With a portable x-ray unit using radio-cobalt, art experts in Japan were able to "see through" ancient bronze temple statues. The shadow pictures told whether the statue was cast all in one piece, and whether different metals were used. Often this information made it possible to discover who the original artist was and at about what date the piece was made.

A few years ago, scientists at the University of Chicago developed an exact way of telling the age of relics

Scientists use radio-isotopes to determine the age of relics.

found in ancient ruins and monuments. This clever method is called *carbon dating*, because it makes use of radio-carbon, which has a half-life of 5,600 years. This isotope is not made in a reactor but is being formed all the time by the action of cosmic rays on nitrogen atoms in the air. As the radio-carbon forms, it is taken up by plants. Animals that eat these plants get the active material into their bodies. When the plant or animal dies, it stops taking in fresh radio-carbon and that is when the number of active atoms begins to drop off. By measuring the activity that remains, scientists can tell how long ago the plant or animal lived. In this way, cloth, grain and wood taken from Egyptian tombs have been found to be about 4,500 years old. Objects in a cave dwelling in southern France date back farther than anything measured so far—about 15,000 years.

The Atomic Energy Commission is spending about 60 million dollars a year on radio-isotope production and equipment, and more than half a million dollars' worth of these active materials is sold each year. Through the use of these isotopes, various industries are saving over 200 times this sum!

Meanwhile, new reactors are being set up in many countries. As radio-isotopes become more plentiful, they should also become cheaper, and so more widely used for many purposes. In the years to come, we can look forward to even more progress than in the past. Out of the atom will come safer drugs, new methods of treating disease, better and more wholesome foods, new plastics and hundreds of other things for better living.

Man first learned to use fire, then the power of steam, and later electricity. Today he stands at the door of a new age—the Age of the Atom. The things to come he can only imagine.

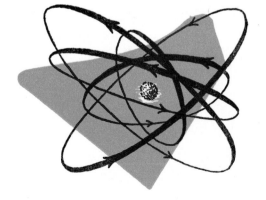

Index

Index

Index

About the Author of This Book

DR. IRA M. FREEMAN lives in New Jersey, where he is associate professor at Rutgers University. Besides his scientific research and the writing of several technical books in his field, he has devoted great effort to interpreting science to the layman. In this connection, he spent a year in Paris recently as a consultant to the United Nations Educational Scientific and Cultural Organization (UNESCO). There he was engaged in developing methods for the teaching and popularization of science for member nations.

In addition to his teaching and writing, Dr. Freeman serves as associate editor of the *American Journal of Physics* and is science consultant to Coronet Instructional Films.

His own science books for young readers have proved very popular over a number of years. They include *Fun with Science, Fun with Chemistry, Fun with Astronomy, Fun with Figures,* and *All About the Wonders of Chemistry.*

About the Illustrator of This Book

GEORGE A. WILDE is originally from Philadelphia, where he attended the Philadelphia Museum School of Art and the Pennsylvania Academy of Fine Arts. From the latter school he received two Cresson Traveling Scholarships which enabled him to study and travel abroad for two years. He then worked in art studios and did free-lance work in Philadelphia and Pittsburgh.

Now he is living in Rowayton, Connecticut, with his wife and daughter, and is specializing in illustration for children.

DATE DUE

DEMCO 38-297